THE NATURE OF METALS

SERIES FOR SELF-EDUCATION

THE NATURE OF
METALS

BRUCE A. ROGERS

Formerly Professor of Mechanical
Engineering and Research Engineer
Agricultural and Mechanical College of Texas

PUBLISHED JOINTLY BY

American Society for Metals, Cleveland, Ohio
The Iowa State University Press, Ames, Iowa

The Author

BRUCE A. ROGERS has maintained a life-long interest in physics and metallurgy. Before his appointment as Professor of Mechanical Engineering and Research Engineer at the Agricultural and Mechanical College of Texas, he had been Professor of Chemistry and Senior Metallurgist with the Institute for Atomic Research at Iowa State University. His doctorate from Harvard University was unique for having been granted for studies in both physics and metallurgy. Throughout his career Dr. Rogers has held academic positions as well as research posts in industry and government and his metallurgical interests have ranged from the practical problems of steel production to research in unusual and nuclear metals.

ⓒ 1964 by The American Society for Metals.

All rights reserved.

Composed and printed by
The Iowa State University Press, Ames, Iowa, U.S.A.
First edition, 1951
  Reprinted, 1957
Second edition, 1964

Library of Congress Card Number: 64–13375

Table of Contents

Introduction

ONE OF THE FIRST DUTIES of an author is to state what he is writing about, how he intends to treat his subject and to whom his book is addressed. Then, the potential reader has an opportunity to decide at once whether he wishes to examine the material presented or to put the book back on the shelf (assuming that he is a tidy person) and turn to things which appear more important to him.

As the title indicates, this book is concerned with the metals. Like many other words in the English language, *metal* is burdened with a multiplicity of meanings. In the scientific sense, a metal is a chemical element which, in the solid state, has a high conductivity for heat and electricity and a lustrous appearance when clean. A metallurgist usually does not speak of the combination of two or more metallic elements as a metal but as an alloy. For example, he calls the combination of copper and zinc either *brass* or *copper-zinc alloy*. In only a few instances do alloys have special names. These are, mainly, either very old ones such as *brass* or *bronze,* or recently coined ones such as *Monel metal* which is the manufacturer's name for a copper-nickel alloy of a definite composition. *Duralumin* and *Stellite* are alloys named by their producers. Although one should say, in the strict sense, metals *and* alloys when referring to the group of substances having a metallic nature, instances do arise when convenience suggests that metal be used to mean an alloy and occasionally it will have that sense in this book.

The treatment of the subject may be indicated by specifying both what the book is intended to do and what it is not intended to do. To put the second matter first, it is not intended to describe how metals are extracted from their ores. It will take only incidental notice of such important historical matters as the effect of metals on human society. Even the properties of metals which make them useful will be a secondary consideration. The book is intended to give its readers some idea of the nature and behavior of metals.

The book is not addressed to metallurgists but to persons who wish to know about metals either because of immediate need or because of a desire to expand their scientific and technical knowledge. Readers will progress more rapidly if they have had one or two years of chemistry and physics but even without this background will not have serious difficulty in understanding the ideas presented.

INTRODUCTION TO SECOND EDITION

This, the second edition of *The Nature of Metals*, is intended for reading by individuals with backgrounds similar to those described in the introduction to the first edition. At least the degree of advancement has not consciously been increased. Two new chapters, Chapters 15 and 16, have been added to provide information on subjects that either were still in the developing stage or were classified when the first edition was written. Chapters 11 and 12 which cover, mainly, old material but are new to this edition will be of interest particularly to readers who wish to increase their knowledge of metallurgy. This class of readers appears to be greater than the author anticipated when writing the first edition. Some changes and additions in other chapters will add to the value of the book for all types of readers.

The Metals

It is now 2,000 years since Julius Caesar was stabbed in a small auditorium known as Pompey's Curia and his body cremated in the Roman Forum. Since that time, many changes have taken place. Yet, in a sense, many things have remained the same. Steel is still the basic material of armaments, although, to be sure, it is not used in the manufacture of shields and short swords. Gold, silver, and copper are, as 2,000 years ago, the principal coinage metals.[1] Bronze is still used for objects intended to resist the corrosive action of the atmosphere, but now it has many competitors.

Knowledge of the metals, of course, has increased greatly since Caesar's day. Yet, the average citizen might have difficulty in naming more than twice as many metals as a Roman could. The Roman world knew, at least, copper, lead, gold, silver, tin, iron, mercury, and zinc

[1] Nor is nickel new as a component of coins. Although the Romans appear not to have produced coins containing nickel, their contemporaries, the Bactrians, made copper-nickel coins containing 20% nickel or more. (See Caley 2.)

(in a copper alloy). To this list, the twentieth-century's man in the street might add aluminum, magnesium, nickel, chromium, cobalt, tungsten, molybdenum, uranium, and one or two others. If he happened to be interested in aeronautics, he might add titanium. Almost certainly, he would be unable to name more than a third of the known metals.

Questions now arise as to how metals may be distinguished from nonmetals and how many metals are known.

WHICH CHEMICAL ELEMENTS ARE METALS?

Both iron and oxygen are chemical elements but only the first is a metal. One asks, "On what basis is this distinction made?" On a chemical basis, little distinction can be made. Both metals and nonmetals enter actively into chemical reactions. The difference reveals itself in the physical properties. By common agreement, those elements that possess high electrical conductivity and a lustrous appearance in the solid state are considered to be metals.

THE PERIODIC TABLE

When all of the metals are to be considered as a group, an advantage may be gained if their names are set down in tabular form as shown in Fig. 1.1. This table is a modification of an arrangement made by the Russian chemist Mendelyev about 1870. In it, the elements are placed in the order of the strength of the positive electrical charge on the nuclei of their atoms. This strength is indicated by the number in the box above each element. Not only does this number, called the "atomic number," indicate the charge on the nucleus but it specifies, also, the number of electrons surrounding the nucleus. The combined charge of the electron "cloud"— that is, the outer portion of the atom—must be equal in magnitude and opposite in sign to the charge on the nucleus. Otherwise, the atom would not be electrically neutral. The nature of the electron cloud is very important because it determines the chemical and physical properties of the element.

Figure 1.1 makes possible a quick determination of whether an element is a metal or a nonmetal. Elements to the left of the heavy, stepped line near the right of the table are metals. Elements to the right of this line are not metals although those immediately to the right, boron, silicon, selenium, tellurium and polonium, are sufficiently metal-like to be called "metalloids."

A BIT OF HISTORY

While the periodic table is being considered, two points of historical interest may be mentioned. The first refers to the names of metals. One notes that many of the names end in "ium." They are the more recently discovered metals, mainly those found in the nineteenth and twentieth centuries. The metals known to the ancient world and those discovered in later times into the eighteenth century were named before the -ium system was established. Examples of such metals are iron, lead, copper, and zinc.

The second point concerns "naturally occurring" and "artificial" elements. With the exception of numbers 43, 61, 85, and 87, all of the elements up to and including 92, uranium, have been found in nature, mainly in ores. Some doubt exists as to whether elements 43 and 61 occur naturally. If they do, the amounts are near the limit of detectability. The four elements mentioned and all of those with numbers higher than 92 have been produced artificially during research related to atomic weapons and nuclear reactors. Including those made artificially, 103 elements are known, of which approximately 75% are metals.

SOME INTERESTING RELATIONSHIPS

A study of the periodic table reveals that the position of an element in the table may give an indication of its

Group → / Period ↓	1	2	3	4	5	6	7	8	9	10	11	12	13	14	15	16	17	18
1																	1 Hydrogen	2 Helium
2	3 Lithium	4 Beryllium											5 Boron	6 Carbon	7 Nitrogen	8 Oxygen	9 Fluorine	10 Neon
3	11 Sodium	12 Magnesium	13 Aluminum											14 Silicon	15 Phosphorus	16 Sulphur	17 Chlorine	18 Argon
4	19 Potassium	20 Calcium	21 Scandium	22 Titanium	23 Vanadium	24 Chromium	25 Manganese	26 Iron	27 Cobalt	28 Nickel	29 Copper	30 Zinc	31 Gallium	32 Germanium	33 Arsenic	34 Selenium	35 Bromine	36 Krypton
5	37 Rubidium	38 Strontium	39 Yttrium	40 Zirconium	41 Columbium	42 Molybdenum	43 Technetium	44 Ruthenium	45 Rhodium	46 Palladium	47 Silver	48 Cadmium	49 Indium	50 Tin	51 Antimony	52 Tellurium	53 Iodine	54 Xenon
6	55 Cesium	56 Barium	57 Lanthanum	72 Hafnium	73 Tantalum	74 Tungsten	75 Rhenium	76 Osmium	77 Iridium	78 Platinum	79 Gold	80 Mercury	81 Thallium	82 Lead	83 Bismuth	84 Polonium	85 Astatine	86 Radon
7	87 Francium	88 Radium	89 Actinium															

Rare Earth Metals

Lanthanide

58 Cerium	59 Praseodymium	60 Neodymium	61 Promethium	62 Samarium	63 Europium	64 Gadolinium	65 Terbium	66 Dysprosium	67 Holmium	68 Erbium	69 Thulium	70 Ytterbium	71 Lutetium

Actinide

90 Thorium	91 Protactinium	92 Uranium	93 Neptunium	94 Plutonium	95 Americium	96 Curium	97 Berkelium	98 Californium	99 Einsteinium	100 Fermium	101 Mendelevium	102 Nobelium	103 Lawrencium

properties. One of the most striking examples is that all[2] or nearly all of the elements in the first ten columns have positive magnetic susceptibilities, that is they are paramagnetic. On the other hand, all elements in columns to the right of the tenth, with the exception of oxygen, have negative magnetic susceptibilities, or are diamagnetic. Furthermore, the metals that are ferro-

---

Fig. 1.1   The Periodic Table of the Elements

This table shows the known elements in the order of the strength of the electrical charge on their nuclei, or inner portions. Elements in the same column are usually similar chemically. At least 88 of the first 92 elements are found in nature. Elements 93 and above were produced synthetically during and after the development of the atomic bomb. Elements to the left of the heavy zig-zag line are metals. Those to the right are nonmetals, although boron, silicon, carbon, selenium, and tellurium are sufficiently metallic in character to be called *metalloids*. Elements in the two strips below the main table are called *rare earths*. The upper strip contains the lanthanide series. These elements have such close chemical similarities that separation of some of them has been difficult. Most of the actinide series, lower strip, show radioactivity.

In September 1949, the International Union of Chemistry met at Amsterdam and recommended that tungsten henceforth be called wolfram, columbium be called niobium and beryllium be renamed glucinium. Although chemists in the United States have accepted the change from columbium to niobium, many, if not most, metallurgists have not. The other two suggested changes have not made headway. The Union recommended also that the names of elements 71 and 91 be spelled lutetium and protactinium, respectively. This recommendation has been followed.

---

[2] A high probability exists that all of them have positive susceptibilities. A negative value for beryllium is likely to be the result of overcorrection for iron present in the specimen. Two other negative values are for metals that were difficult to obtain in the pure state at the time the measurements were made.

magnetic, that is are magnetic in the sense that iron is, all lie in the same horizontal line. There are three of them: iron, nickel, and cobalt: elements 26, 27, and 28, respectively. Another interesting fact is that metals in the same column of the periodic table often have similar chemical and physical properties. For example, the three metals of highest electrical conductivity, copper, silver, and gold, all lie in column 11. The three metals in column 4 have the property of absorbing astonishing amounts of oxygen and nitrogen at relatively low temperatures. Even a moderate amount of absorbed gas makes them very brittle although their external appearance may give no indication of their changed condition. This brittleness caused considerable trouble when production was undertaken and required special procedures for melting and hot fabrication. The precious metals, not including silver and gold, lie in a group that includes elements 44, 45, 46, 76, 77, and 78.

THE RARE EARTHS

No mention has yet been made of the two rows in the lower part of Fig. 1.1. These two series of elements usually are called the "rare earths." The upper one is called the lanthanide series because it fits in the periodic table immediately after lanthanum. Frequently lanthanum is included in this group because of some chemical similarity and as a convenience in description. Occasionally yttrium is classed as a rare earth. The lower row has been named the actinide series because it follows immediately after actinium.

THE LANTHANIDE SERIES

The lanthanide series was established before chemists were aware that an actinide series existed. It was once considered to comprise all of the rare earths. As to why elements in this group should be called rare earths, the answer is that they should not because some of them are not more rare than a number of well-known metals. Curiously, those with odd atomic numbers are less abundant than those with even numbers. The next point that needs explanation is why all of them are combined into one group that is located between lanthanum and hafnium. The reason is that because of their unusually close chemical similarity, chemists found them very difficult to separate at first. Recent developments have made their separation easier and further investigation has shown that their properties are more diverse than was once believed. Although they are not generally suitable for making objects in the way that steel or brass are, they do have interesting and sometimes valuable properties. For example, gadolinium is ferromagnetic in the manner of iron when cold but loses this property if heated above 16° C. Hence, the metal is magnetic on a cold day but not on a warm one.

THE ACTINIDE SERIES

The actinide metals thorium and uranium have been known for a relatively long time and are not particularly scarce. That they belonged to another series resembling the lanthanides was not realized until some of the other actinide elements had been obtained and their properties determined. These other elements are very scarce because only small amounts of them are produced in the course of nuclear activities. Even when formed they undergo radioactive[3] changes into elements of lower atomic number and cease to exist. Even the naturally occurring elements thorium, protactinium, and uranium, eventually disappear. Protactinium does so in a relatively short time but thorium and uranium continue to disintegrate slowly over periods of billions or trillions

---

[3] Radioactivity will be explained in more detail in Chapter 16.

of years. Given enough time, all three elements are converted to nonradioactive lead or bismuth.

REFERENCES

1. H. V. Morton: "A Traveler in Rome," Dodd Mead & Company, New York, 1957, pp. 86–89.
2. Earle Radcliffe Caley: "The Composition of Ancient Greek Bronze Coins," The American Philosophical Society, Philadelphia, 1939, pp. 155–156.

CHAPTER 2

Looking Inside the Metals

A PERSON who is curious about how a thing is made is likely to try to take it apart or to look inside of it. Taking a metal apart in a way that would permit one to see how it is put together is not a simple problem. However, methods do exist that, in effect, let a person look inside.

THE MICROSCOPE

Of the devices that have been used in studying the structure of metals, the microscope probably has yielded the most information. Unfortunately, in the study of metals, the microscope is handicapped by a difficulty that does not exist when it is applied to biological investigation. To determine the nature of an animal or vegetable substance, a biologist cuts off a very thin layer through which he passes a beam of light so that he can see into its interior. As even the thinnest sections of metal are opaque, the metallurgist must use a different procedure. First, he polishes a specimen until it is very smooth and flat. If he leaves the surface uneven, the low portions are out of focus when the microscope is adjusted for the high areas and the high portions will appear fuzzy when the microscope gives a sharp image of the low regions. Second, he must devise some method for bringing out details because the smoothly polished metal may simply act as a mirror. Etching the polished surface with an acid or some other chemical reagent is the most common method of bringing out a structure.

Figure 2.1 shows a polished and etched section of cast copper as it appears under the microscope at a magnification of 75 diameters. This photograph—or photomicrograph as it is called by the metallographers who take such pictures—represents a part of the surface with a diameter of about 1/20 in. In terms of area, the picture corresponds to only 0.002 sq. in., that is, less than the size of a small pinhead. Because only a small region can be seen at one time, metallographers usually examine several areas of a specimen.

The photograph shows that copper actually is an aggregate of individual grains fitted accurately together. As the result of the etching action, each grain is delineated by boundary lines and also has a distinct shading. Extensive investigations have shown that all metals are made up in much the same way. Of course, the polished and etched surface can show only the cross section of the assemblage of grains, and the grain boundary network represents only the traces of the surfaces over which the grains are in contact. That the grains adhere strongly to each other is evident from the high strength of metals. In some instances, the grains are much smaller than those in Fig. 2.1, none of which are entirely in the field of view; in others, they are considerably larger.

HOW ETCHING REVEALS STRUCTURE

Etching reagents differ in their action on metals. Accordingly the character of the etched surface cannot be

Fig. 2.1 Copper—Polished Smooth and Etched

The picture was taken at a magnification of 75 diameters. Hence, it represents a portion of the metal about 1 mm. in diameter. In English units, the diameter is considerably less than ¹⁄₁₆ in. and the area is about 0.002 sq. in. The photograph shows that the metal is composed of individual grains which are made evident both by boundary lines and by a difference in shading.

Courtesy, H. M. Schleicher, American Metal Co., Ltd.

Magnification, 75×

interpreted without consideration of the reagent. For this reason, some illustrations of etching action are desirable.

In Fig. 2.1, the individual grains were made evident not only by the boundary lines but also by the differences in shading. Figure 2.2 shows a piece of iron in which the existence of different grains is made apparent only by the tiny troughlike boundaries between them. The interior portions of the grains are featureless. Probably the length of time during which the etching reagent (1% nitric acid and 99% ethyl alcohol) remained in contact with the surface had much to do with the absence of at-

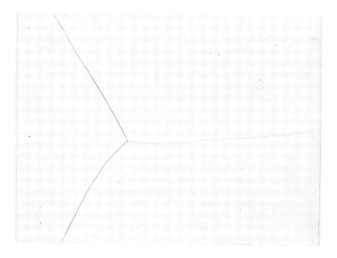

Fig. 2.2   Grain Boundaries in Pure Iron

The iron was polished and etched with a solution of 1% nitric acid in ethyl alcohol. The boundary lines actually are tiny troughs produced as the result of atoms of iron being dissolved rapidly at the intergranular surfaces.

Cleaves and Hiegel (*1*).   Magnification, 250×

tack on the interior areas. A longer etching period might
well have produced some sort of pattern on the surface.

Some reagents do not etch out a troughlike network
of lines to mark the boundaries between the grains.
Rather, they form on the polished surface a layer of reaction products that varies in thickness, hence in color,
from grain to grain. Copper and its alloys frequently
are etched with a reagent of this kind. The result is
illustrated by the photomicrograph of beta brass shown
in Fig. 2.3.[1] In this instance, the variation in the shading
of the grains probably is due mainly to differences in
thickness of a layer of oxide. The specimen was etched
with a reagent that had a combined oxidizing and oxide-
dissolving effect—that is, one component formed an oxide
layer and the other component dissolved it. Probably
the rate of formation of the oxide layer depended upon
the orientation[2] of the grain, whereas, the rate of solution of the layer was less dependent upon orientation.
Hence, the thickness of the coating varied from grain to
grain.

If the composition of an alloy varies from point to
point over the polished surface, that fact may sometimes
be revealed by a suitable etchant. Examples of such variation will be found in Chapter 6 on "Solidification" but
a striking illustration is presented in Fig. 2.4. This
photomicrograph shows the effect of boiling sodium picrate solution on a specimen of cast manganese steel. This
reagent forms a dark adherent deposit on areas that
contain carbon but has little effect on carbon-free areas.
In the figure, the light areas represent regions that solidi-

---

[1] For the meaning of beta brass see Chapter 5, Fig. 5.11, and also
Chapter 11. This specimen contained 52.3% copper and 47.7% zinc.
[2] Orientation refers, in this instance, to the position or direction of
specific lines and planes of atoms in a grain relative to the plane
of the polished surface. The significance of orientation will be
understood better after a reading of Chapter 3.

Fig. 2.3   Coloring of Grains of Beta Brass

This brass was etched with a solution of ferric chloride and
hydrochloric acid. The difference in shading is mainly the
result of the difference in the thickness of a thin film of
products resulting from the attack of the etching reagent.
Courtesy, Division of Metallurgy, National Bureau of Standards.   Magnification, 20×

---

fied first, and the dark areas, the portions that solidified
last. Obviously, the parts that solidified first contain relatively little carbon as they have scarcely been darkened
at all.

THE REMOVAL OF METAL BY ETCHING REAGENTS

The photomicrographs shown in Fig. 2.1 and Fig. 2.2
indicate that etching action in these instances involved

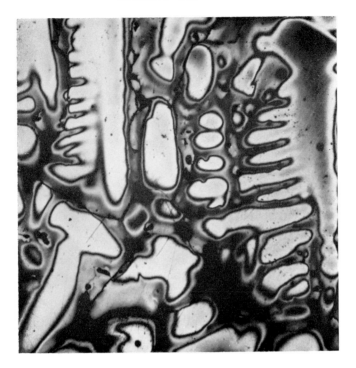

Fig. 2.4 Carbon Revealed by Sodium Picrate

Areas that contain carbon are blackened by the deposit formed by this reagent; areas that do not contain carbon are not affected.

Courtesy, F. F. Lucas, Bell Telephone Laboratories, Inc.

Magnification, 300×

the removal of a thin layer of metal. The removal could not have been uniform or no structure would have been revealed, and it must have been related to the nature of the specimen. Troughlike grain boundaries such as those shown in Fig. 2.2 suggest that the atoms in an intergranular surface are more readily taken into solution than those in the body of a grain. Put in another way, the atoms at the contact between grains probably do not fit exactly into the arrangement of atoms in either grain and can be dislodged with relative ease. The tendency for atoms in the grain boundaries to be detached readily is evident also in the behavior of iron heated in a vacuum or in a nonoxidizing atmosphere. At about 700°C., grain boundaries similar to those in Fig. 2.2 develop rapidly in iron, apparently because of the evaporation of atoms. Boundaries formed when iron is heated under hydrogen may be seen in Fig. 9.2.

In the interior areas of grains, removal by etching often develops a pattern that differs from grain to grain depending on the orientation of the grain with respect to the polished cross section. An example of such patterns is presented in Fig. 2.5 which is an electron micrograph of magnesium at 9,000 diameters. In the figure, the distinct patterns in the three grains stand out clearly. At lower magnifications, the difference in pattern would be evident mainly as a difference in shading resulting from different reflecting powers of different patterns.

Vigorous etching sometimes reveals planes of specific character such as those shown in Fig. 3.1 in the next chapter.

GRAIN BOUNDARIES UNDER THE MICROSCOPE

The reason that boundaries like those in Fig. 2.2 are visible under a microscope may be understood from an examination of Fig. 2.6. In metallographic work, the surface of the specimen usually is illuminated by a beam of light that enters the microscope from the side and is reflected downward on to the specimen by a glass reflecting plate identified as G in the figure. If the surface of the specimen is perpendicular to the axis of the microscope tube, the rays are reflected upward through the reflecting plate to the eyepiece, but any part of the surface which is not perpendicular will not reflect the full intensity of light and so appears darkened.

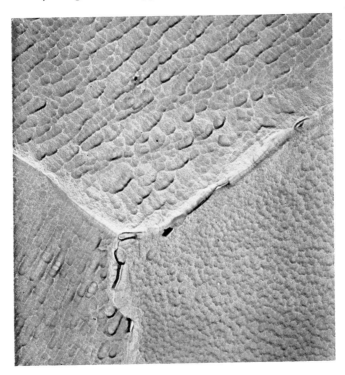

Fig. 2.5   Etching Patterns on a Magnesium Alloy

This high-magnification micrograph was taken with an electron microscope. Etching produces a characteristic pattern on all metals if allowed to proceed sufficiently long. At high magnifications, such patterns may stand out clearly as in this photomicrograph. At low magnifications, they contribute to a difference in shading among the grains.

Heidenreich, Gerould and McNulty (4).

Magnification, 9000×

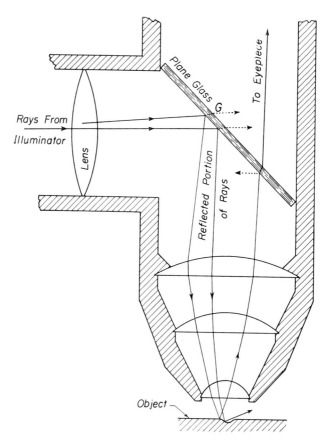

Fig. 2.6 Light Rays in a Metallurgical Microscope

The light from a bright point source enters through a lens at the left and is reflected downward onto the specimen. If the surface of the specimen is perpendicular to the axis of the microscope, it reflects the light to the eyepiece, with maximum intensity. If the surface is not perpendicular the rays are deflected and produce less effect at the eyepiece.

A COIN OF TIBERIUS CAESAR

Examination of an object with a microscope may reveal information about its composition or the manner in which it was made. However, for greater certainty, confirming evidence from other types of investigation usually is desirable. An illustration of what the microscope can indicate is given by Fig. 2.7 which shows a "bronze" coin made during the reign of Tiberius Caesar (14 A.D. to 37 A.D.). The magnification of this photomicrograph is not known but probably is in the range from 200 to 400 diameters. Very likely, the coin did not contain enough tin to be considered a true bronze. Much "bronze" coinage of this period actually was copper coinage. Tin was not plentiful in early Imperial times. That metal had become decreasingly available since the fall of Carthage (146 B.C.) and the destruction of the Carthaginian merchant fleet that had been bringing it into the Mediterranean region from Spain or Cornwall or from wherever it came.

Figure 2.7 does not give complete information about the coin but does reveal some facts. The elongated blobs are almost certainly lead. One might estimate a lead content of 2 or 3%. The deformed parallelograms, such as those marked a suggest two things to an experienced metallurgist. First, they tell him that the alloy from which the coin was stamped had been worked, or fabricated, and then reheated before the stamping operation. Parallelograms of this type are not found in cast copper or bronze. They appear only if the metal has been worked in the cold condition and reheated afterwards. Secondly, the appearance of the parallelograms suggests that the coin probably was struck while hot. The parallelograms—called "twins" by metallurgists—have straight sides in metal not deformed after annealing (reheating). The idea that the coin was struck hot is in agreement with information from other sources.

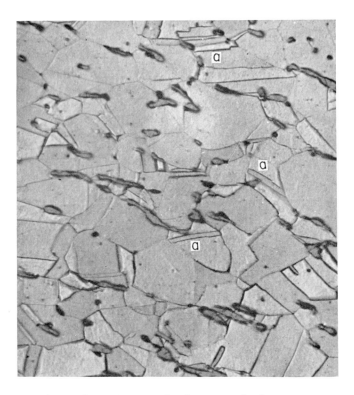

Fig. 2.7 Photomicrograph of a Coin of Tiberius Caesar

This coin probably should be called a copper rather than a bronze coin. The tin content of most copper base coins was low during the time of Tiberius because of the general scarcity of tin during the period. The elongated gray blobs indicate lead which was a constituent of many ancient "bronze" coins. The deformed parallelograms marked *a* and similar bands indicate that the metal had been worked cold and reheated before the stamping operation. Ancient coins usually were stamped hot.

Courtesy, C. K. Dosch, A & M College of Texas.

Magnification, 300× (estimated)

THE ELECTRON MICROSCOPE

For practical purposes, the ordinary, optical microscope is limited to magnifications of perhaps 2,000 or
3,000 diameters. During the 1930's, a microscope of a
different type was developed. It became known as an
"electron microscope" because its operation depends on
streams of electrons instead of light rays. It provides
magnifications many times higher than can be obtained
with the best optical instruments but it has some disadvantages too. It is expensive and usually requires
considerable skill and patience on the part of the oper-
ator.

The electron microscope is essentially a transmission
instrument but pictures can be obtained by reflection if
the electrons strike the specimen at an angle instead of
from a perpendicular direction. However, because of
this angle, the image is distorted considerably except
over a narrow central strip. Use of the microscope in
this way is likely to be limited to special problems.

Because the beam of electrons cannot pass through a
piece of metal thicker than 1/100,000 centimeter, nearly
all early work with the electron microscope was done by
a "replica" method. Some materials such as the plastic,
Formvar, can be used to obtain a thin layer of substance
—a replica—that reproduces faithfully the irregularities
in the surface of a specimen and is relatively transparent
to electrons. The replica can be used instead of the
original specimen in the electron microscope. Figure 2.8,
which shows a replica and a photographic plate but
leaves out the magnetic lenses and other details, gives an
idea of the replica method. Suppose that the specimen
is a very simple one with two grain boundaries but an
otherwise smooth surface. The stream of electrons e
coming through the replica r of the specimen is reduced
in intensity at all points but especially so where the
replica is thick. Correspondingly, the photographic film

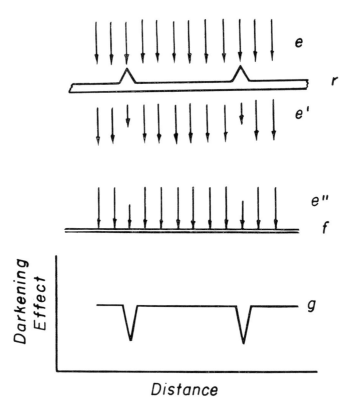

Fig. 2.8 How Details in a Replica Are Reproduced on a Photographic Film

This diagram shows only the replica, r, the film, f, and the stream of electrons, e. Details of the microscope have been omitted. The intensity of the beam of electrons at any point is reduced in proportion to the thickness of the replica. On the film, each point is darkened according to the density of the electron stream that reaches it as shown in graph g. This figure is based on a "negative" replica, that is, the low points of the replica correspond to the high points of the original surface. Positive replicas that are copies of the original surface may also be made. See Zworykin (6).

is darkened least in the two regions corresponding to the grain boundaries. This situation is made evident by graph *g* which does not, however, indicate the magnification that actually occurs. Finally, photographing of the film yields a further magnified picture of the original surface. Other procedures for making replicas are also

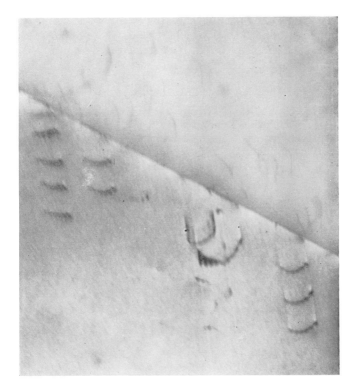

Fig. 2.9   A Transmission Electron Micrograph of a Thin Sheet of Stainless Steel

The markings in this picture are explained in Chapter 15.
Whelan, Hirsch, Horne, and Bollman (7).

Magnification, 33,000×

used. One that involves the making of a second replica from the first was used to get the electron micrograph of magnesium shown in Fig. 2.5.

In the late 1950's, several investigators were successful in taking transmission pictures of metal samples made very thin by a combination of machining and chemical attack. An example of such a micrograph is presented in Fig. 2.9. The peculiar markings observed in this specimen of stainless steel will be explained in Chapter 15. In a photograph such as this one, one truly gets a glimpse inside a metal.

REFERENCES

1. Harold E. Cleaves and John M. Hiegel: "Properties of High-Purity Iron," *Bureau of Standards Journal of Research,* Vol. 28, 1942, pp. 643–667.

2. Henry S. Rawdon and Marjorie G. Lorentz: "Metallographic Etching Reagents: I, for Copper," *Bureau of Standards Scientific Papers,* Vol. 16, 1920, pp. 641–668.

3. John Howe Hall: "Studies of Hadfield's Manganese Steel With the Highpower Microscope," *Transactions,* American Institute of Mining and Metallurgical Engineers, Vol. 84, 1929, pp. 382–427.

4. R. D. Heidenreich, C. H. Gerould, and R. E. McNulty: "Electron Metallographic Methods and Some Results for Magnesium Alloys," *Transactions,* American Institute of Mining and Metallurgical Engineers, Vol. 166, 1946, pp. 15–36.

5. D. H. Page: "Reflection Electron Microscopy at High Angles," *British Journal of Applied Physics,* Vol. 9, 1958, pp. 60–67.

6. V. K. Zworykin: "Applications of the Electron Microscope in Metallurgy," *Transactions,* American Institute of Mining and Metallurgical Engineers, Vol. 152, 1943, pp. 13–37.

7. M. J. Whelan, P. B. Hirsch, R. W. Horne, and W. Bollman: "Dislocations and Stacking Faults in Stainless Steel," *Proceedings,* Royal Society, Ser. A, Vol. 240, 1957, pp. 524–538.

CHAPTER 3

How Atoms Are Arranged in Metals

THE PHOTOMICROGRAPHS of Chapter 2 illustrated some of the ways in which etching reagents act on metals but did not reveal their crystalline nature. Deeper etching sometimes brings out the crystalline character of metals and does so because specific planes in a metal crystal are more resistant to the etching reagent than others and so stand out in the manner of the visible planes of a mineral crystal. This effect is illustrated in Fig. 3.1 which shows deeply etched aluminum at 5,000 diameters. Apparently, planes which correspond to the sides of cubes are most resistant in aluminum (at least to the etching reagent used) as they are the ones that remain. The blocks in the upper right area of this figure lie in a different position, or orientation, from those in the lower left area. This condition is to be anticipated as the grain boundary that crosses the micrograph in a northwest-southeast direction indicates that the areas belong to different grains, and, as explained below, the crystal orientation in one grain usually is not specifically related to the orientation in a neighboring grain.

Fig. 3.1   Deeply Etched Aluminum at 5000 X

The planes appearing in the photograph are those most resistant to the etching reagent. The difference in orientation
of the tiny blocks indicates that the upper right and lower
left areas belong to different crystals. This photograph was
taken with an electron microscope.

Mahl (*1*).   Magnification, 5000×

METALLIC CRYSTALS FORMED BY FREEZING

Some metals, of which bismuth is one, reveal their
crystalline character by the manner in which they solidify. Figure 3.2 exhibits crystals that were formed when a
hemispherical container filled with liquid bismuth was
held motionless until the metal partly solidified and
was then inverted so that the liquid portion ran out.
The straight sides and nearly right angles are evidence
that metallic crystals grow by adding atoms on specific

Fig. 3.2 Crystals of Bismuth

These crystals were formed when a container filled with liquid bismuth was held motionless until the metal partially solidified and was then inverted so that the liquid portion ran out.

---

planes. The crystals show some tendency toward similar orientation, apparently, because of the downward flow of heat during solidification; in general, the direction of flow of heat influences the orientation of the crystals. On the other hand, when cooling is very slow and the temperature is uniform throughout the body of metal, crystals form more or less simultaneously throughout the mass and with quite unrelated orientations. They start as tiny solid particles and grow by acquiring atoms of metal from the liquid until they encounter adjoining crystals and so form grains like those exhibited in Chapter 2.

WHAT X-RAYS YIELD

Indicative as Fig. 3.1 and Fig. 3.2 are of the crystalline character of metals, they do not reveal the details of the arrangement of atoms. For this information, one must use X-rays. Several procedures are available for X-ray investigations. None of them yields pictures as interesting as those in Chapter 2 but gives, instead, a pattern of spots or lines from which calculations can be made. As an example, a pattern obtained on tantalum is presented in Fig. 3.3. This kind of pattern is called an "X-ray diffraction powder pattern" because it is obtained by the passage of a fine beam of X-rays through a "powder" of fine filings of the metal.

HOW THE POWDER PATTERN IS OBTAINED

A powder pattern like that in Fig. 3.3 may be produced with relatively simple apparatus. The X-ray source is not shown but an idea of how the pattern is obtained may be gained from Fig. 3.4a and Fig. 3.4b. In

Fig. 3.3   X-ray Diffraction Powder Pattern for Tantalum

While the film was being exposed, it was bent into circular form so that it would fit inside the circle in the next figure. Rays entered through the hole at h. Those passing through the sample without being reflected struck the film at a. From this film, one can calculate the dimensions of the unit cell of tantalum.

the first figure, f is the strip of photographic film on which the pattern is formed. It is held in circular shape by being forced against the inner wall of a circular, light-tight box. The sample of powder for which the pattern is desired is located at the center of the circle. A hypothetical plane in one of the particles is shown in two positions, p and p'. The sample is rotated continuously about an axis perpendicular to the paper so that as many planes as possible in the different particles come into position to reflect the X-rays coming in from the left. Why the sample produces a line spectrum rather than a continuous spectrum will become apparent.

Planes in a crystal do not reflect X-rays as a mirror reflects light. Light rays are reflected from a surface, a single plane, but X-rays are reflected by the cooperation of many parallel, atom-bearing planes. To produce a line on a pattern such as Fig. 3.3, three factors must be related in an exact way. The factors are:

(1) the distance between planes, usually called "d"
(2) the wave length of the X-rays, customarily called "λ."
(3) the angle at which the X-ray beam strikes the planes, indicated by "θ."

To understand how these factors should be related, one should study Fig. 3.4b.

Figure 3.4b pictures a group of parallel planes that lie perpendicular to the plane of the paper. The distance between them is d. Two rays of an incoming X-ray beam of wave length λ[1] strike the two top planes of atoms at an angle θ and are reflected at the same angle. To reach point f, comparable to point c reached by the ray abc, ray def must travel an additional distance xey.

---

[1] X-rays travel by vibratory motion just as light beams or radio beams do and, as assumed above, have a definite wave length. For the beam to exist at all, all parts of it, that is, all rays, must be at the same stage of vibration, or, be in phase.

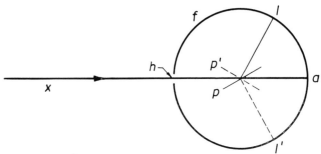

Fig. 3.4a   The Reflection of X-rays by Planes of Atoms

f is a photographic film bent to form a circle
p is the plane of atoms that reflects the X-rays (*p'* is the same
     plane in an equivalent reflecting position)
l is the line made on the film by the reflected ray (*l'* is the line
     made by the plane in position *p'*)
x is the beam of X-rays
h is the hole through which rays enter the camera to strike
     plane *p* (in the sample)
a is the point where X-rays not reflected strike the film.

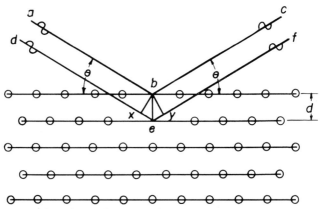

**Fig. 3.4b   The Reflection of an X-ray Beam From a Set
of Parallel Planes**

Only two rays of the beam are shown. For a reflection to
occur, the three factors—distance between planes, *d*; wave
length of the X-rays, λ; and angle of the incoming rays, *θ*—
must have the proper values to make the distance *xey* exactly
equal to one wave length, or to an integral number of wave
lengths. The process that occurs is more truly diffraction than
reflection. For a more complete analysis, see Buerger (*2*).

Hence, when the two rays reach the positions c and f (beam front cf) they will not be in phase unless xey is exactly equal to a wave length λ. Evidently what must be done is to adjust the angle of the incoming rays so that xey will equal λ. Then the different rays will reinforce rather than cancel each other and will produce a line on the pattern. Of course, a line will be produced also if $xey = 2\lambda$. This would be a "second order" reflection.

An experienced X-ray crystallographer can make the calculations from a pattern such as Fig. 3.3 in a short time. From a knowledge of the X-rays used and the angle through which the rays were deflected plus some facts about the metal, he would conclude that the atoms in tantalum are arranged in the same manner as the ping-pong balls in the model of Fig. 3.5. Several other metals, for example, chromium, columbium, molybdenum and iron (at low temperature) yield similar patterns and have their atoms arranged in the same way.

A SIMPLE WAY OF DESCRIBING AN ARRANGEMENT OF ATOMS

If a ping-pong ball model of a complete metal crystal were to be made, it would extend for many feet in all directions. Even the preparation of a model like Fig. 3.5 would be a burdensome way of specifying an arrangement of atoms. Fortunately, a simple scheme is available. How the structure may be indicated simply may be understood from a comparison of Fig. 3.5 with the two figures that follow it. Figure 3.6 shows the same model that appeared in Fig. 3.5 but with a group of nine balls lighted to distinguish them from the others. These nine balls actually constitute a cube with an additional ball at the center. One notes that if this lighted cube were imagined to move about in three perpendicular directions corresponding to the cube edges, and, equivalently, to an imaginary set of axes in a crystal, the move-

Fig. 3.5   Arrangement of Atoms—Body-Centered Cubic

A model of the arrangement of atoms as deduced from a pattern such as the one shown in Fig. 3.3. Besides tantalum, iron, molybdenum, columbium, and some other metals have this structure.

Atom models by courtesy of G. R. Fitterer, University of Pittsburgh.

Fig. 3.6   The Model of Fig. 3.5 With Nine Balls Lighted

These nine balls form a cube with a ball at each corner and one at the center.

ment would, in a sense, generate a model resembling Fig. 3.5 of any size desired. Hence, this one cube specifies the whole structure and one need only to sketch it as has been done in Fig. 3.7. A simple unit of structure such as the one in Fig. 3.7 that is capable of generating the complete structure of a crystal when it is moved about is called a "unit cell." Only the simplest unit of structure that will generate a crystal qualifies as a unit cell. For obvious reasons, the cell just shown is called a "body-centered cubic" unit cell. The structure which it generates is called a body-centered cubic structure.

A point to notice about Fig. 3.7 is that each of the eight balls, or atoms, on the corners of the cube are shared with seven adjoining unit cells. Hence, all eight of them together contribute only the equivalent of one ball to the unit cell. This equivalent ball plus the ball at the center of the cube may be considered properly to

---

Fig. 3.7   The Unit Cell of a Body-Centered Cubic Metal

This unit cell is a sketch of the cube containing nine lighted balls that appears in Fig. 3.6. In this figure, atoms are imagined to be substituted for balls.

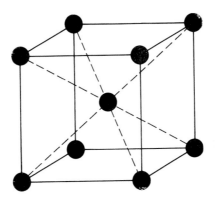

belong to the cell. Calculations show that the weight of metal to be credited to the unit cell actually does correspond to the weight of two atoms.

TWO ADDITIONAL SIMPLE ARRANGEMENTS

X-ray investigations have shown that copper, nickel, platinum, and a number of other metals have atomic arrangements that can be illustrated by the model of Fig. 3.8. Comparison of this model with Fig. 3.9 and Fig. 3.10 indicates that the structure can be represented by the unit cell of Fig. 3.10 as the movement of this cell in the direction of the cube edges could generate the entire structure.

The third common type of atomic arrangement does not have three perpendicular axes with atoms spaced at equal intervals along each. Instead, it has three axes

Fig. 3.8   Arrangement of Atoms—Face-Centered Cubic

A model of the arrangement of atoms in copper, nickel, platinum, and several other metals.

Fig. 3.9 The Model of Fig. 3.8 with 14 Balls Lighted

These lighted balls outline a cube having a lighted ball on each corner and one at the center of each face.

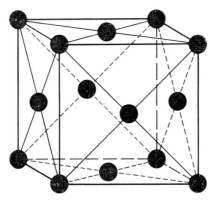

Fig. 3.10 The Unit Cell of a Face-Centered Cubic Metal

In this figure, atoms may be imagined to have been substituted for the balls in Fig. 3.9. Although the cell has 14 atoms associated with it, its volume corresponds to only four atoms. Why this is true becomes obvious after a little thought about the sharing of atoms with neighboring unit cells.

lying in a plane at angles of 120° from each other, counting from the "positive" ends of the axes, plus a fourth axis perpendicular to the plane of the other three. The model that represents this way of arranging atoms is shown in Fig. 3.11. Figures 3.12 and 3.13 help to illustrate the relative positions of the atoms and especially the "symmetry" of the arrangement. Although Fig. 3.13 shows the arrangement of the atoms very well, it contains more of them than are needed to generate the structure; hence, it is not the unit cell. The cell is shown in Fig. 3.14. Also, as one may note, the generation may be accomplished by movement along only two

Fig. 3.11   Arrangement   of   A t o m s—Close-Packed Hexagonal

A model of the arrangement of atoms in magnesium, titanium, zinc, and some other metals. This model was made by piling identical layers of balls so that the balls in any layer lay directly over balls in the second layer below. The top of the model shows that, in the horizontal plane, balls line up in three directions.

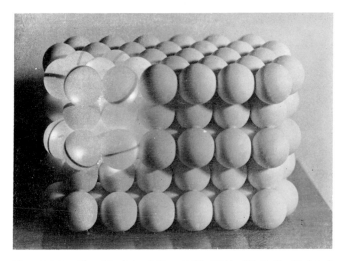

Fig. 3.12   The Model of Fig. 3.11 With 17 Balls Lighted
The top layer of lighted balls forms a hexagon and the entire
assembly outlines a six-sided prism. Many minerals are hexagonal in character and form six-sided crystals but most of them
cannot be classified as close-packed.

---

of the three co-planar axes plus the perpendicular one.
Titanium, magnesium, zinc, and several other metals
have structures of this type. A glance at the last four
figures suggests why these metals are called "close-packed
hexagonal" metals, and correspondingly, why Fig. 3.14
is the "close-packed hexagonal unit cell."

PATTERNS OF COMPLEX STRUCTURES

The X-ray diffraction powder pattern of a face-centered cubic structure is only slightly more complicated
than that of a body-centered cubic one, but patterns of
close-packed hexagonal metals are considerably more so.
Also, more complicated is the pattern produced by a

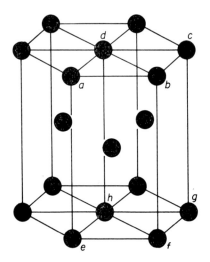

Fig. 3.13   Drawing of the Prism Outlined in Fig. 3.12

A figure of this type is commonly used to illustrate the structure and symmetry of close-packed hexagonal substances. It is not the unit cell, however, as it contains more atoms than are necessary to generate the close-packed hexagonal structure.

metal with an orthorhombic cell, that is, a cell in which the edges of the cell are mutually perpendicular as they are in a cubic cell but differ in length from each other. Uranium has a cell of this type and, as will be seen in Chapter 16 its atomic arrangement is less simple than those described above. Some substances produce such complicated powder patterns that another of the methods of X-ray investigation may be more suitable for the determination of their structures than is the powder pattern.

THE SIZES OF ATOMS

From a pattern like the one in Fig. 3.3, a crystallographer can determine easily the length of the edge of the

Fig. 3.14   The Unit Cell of a Close-Packed Hexagonal Metal

The ratio of height to base dimensions of the cells of metals of this type appears never to have exactly the value corresponding to the stacking of spheres, 1.63. Some metals have a ratio that is too small and some have one that is too large. The unit cell has a volume corresponding to two atoms.

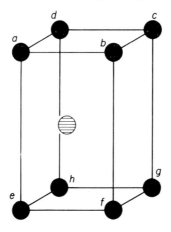

unit cell, that is, the spacing of atoms along a line coinciding with the edge. For example, if he had a pattern for copper, he could calculate quickly the length of an edge of the unit cell in Fig. 3.10. He would find the distance to be 0.000000014205 in. or 0.000000036080 cm. or 3.6080 Å.[2] From this distance he could then determine by the simplest geometry that the distance between centers of nearest atoms is 0.00000001005 in. or 0.00000002551 cm. or 2.551 Å. This distance is, of course, half of the length of the diagonal of one of the faces in Fig.

---

[2] An Ångstrom unit, usually written as Å, is one hundred millionth of a centimeter long. One notes immediately how much more easily one can say that the length of an edge of a unit cell is 3.6080 Å than to state the distance in centimeters.

3.10. A little mental arithmetic indicates that nearly 100,000,000 atoms of copper could be placed along a line one inch long.

SPACE LATTICES

In the previous section, the distance between atoms in a metal with cubic structure was related to the lengths of the edges of the unit cell. Dimensions in an atomic structure may also be indicated as the spacing of atoms along lines that are parallel to cube edges. The spacing turns out to equal the length of an edge of the unit cell. When this method of designation is used the spacing is called a "lattice parameter." The relationship between lattice parameter and unit cell is made more understandable by Fig. 3.15. This figure shows at the bottom a cubic unit cell of primitive type, that is, neither body-centered nor face-centered. Above it is a section of space lattice of which the distance between intersections equals the length of the edges of the unit cell. Obviously, if the unit cell were moved in three perpendicular dimensions in jumps equal to the lengths of its edges, it would generate the lattice.

The lines that are so prominent in Fig. 3.15 have no value except that their intersections fix the positions of the "lattice points" in space. A lattice should not be imagined as a set of lines but as a phantom three-dimensional array of points that is superposed on the substance and is related to the position of its atoms. In a simple metal such as iron or copper, an atom is imagined to be centered on each point.[3] In some substances, the atoms may be considered merely to be associated with the lattice points, the points themselves being unoccupied.

---

[3] For a body-centered cubic metal, two sets of points are needed, one for corner atoms and one for center atoms. A face-centered cubic metal would require four interpenetrating lattices.

Fig. 3.15   Cubic Space Lattice and Unit Cell

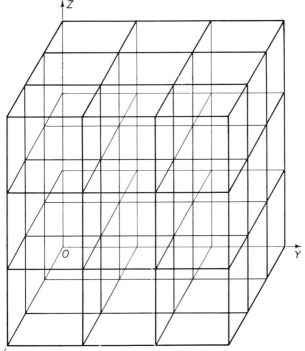

A lattice of this kind may be imagined to be formed by the intersection of three sets of equally spaced and mutually perpendicular sets of planes. The points where three planes intersect (also the points where three lines intersect) are called lattice points. A space lattice of this kind superimposed on a crystal (mentally) can aid in describing the crystal if one remembers that the arrangement of atoms about every lattice point is the same. Of course, this particular lattice would work for only certain kinds of crystals. The unit cell below corresponds to one of the cubic cells shown in the lattice. If the unit cell is imagined to be moved about in three perpendicular directions by translations equal to the length of an edge, it generates the lattice.

If it should happen that the atoms in a substance are not spaced at the same interval in each of the three principal directions, the corresponding unit cell will have edges of unequal lengths and the lattice parameters in different directions will be unequal. For example,

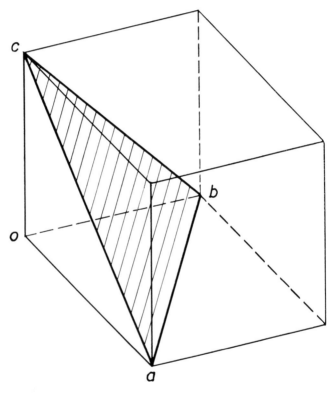

Fig. 3.16   The Position of a Very Important Plane in Face-Centered Cubic Metals

The plane *abc* may be imagined to pass through corners of a cubic model similar to Fig. 3.8. The atoms on such a plane are arranged as shown in the next figure.

the unequal edges of the unit cell of uranium must mean that the lattice parameters in the three directions are unequal. Their lengths are specified as a_o, b_o and c_o.

PLANES THAT REFLECT X-RAYS

The comment already has been made that X-rays are reflected from particular types of planes in a crystal. In the face-centered cubic crystals, one important type of plane is the one that appears as the sides of the model in Fig. 3.8. Another is the diagonal plane abc in Fig. 3.16. An idea of how such a plane looks may be gained from Fig. 3.17 although the angle from which the photograph was taken is not the best for showing how the atoms lie. A clearer view of the same type of plane appears in Fig.13.3. For reasons that will become obvious in a later section, the plane abc is known to crystallographers as a (111) plane.

THE NAMING OF PLANES

Because frequent reference must be made to different types of planes, a convenient way of specifying them is desirable. A satisfactory system was developed years ago by W. H. Miller. Since his time, planes usually have been designated by their "Miller indices."

For crystals with cubic structures, the Miller system is very simple. A set of three mutually perpendicular axes is imagined to be introduced into the crystal. For a metal like copper, these axes will coincide with rows of atoms as depicted in Drawing a of Fig. 3.18. The atoms are spaced a distance a_o apart on all axes, a_o being, also, the length of an edge of a unit cell.

The remaining drawings in this figure illustrate how the Miller indices of several different planes are found. Drawing b shows two parallel planes. The one nearest the origin of the set of axes intercepts those axes at $a_o/2$, $a_o/2$, and $a_o/2$. More simply, the a_o being understood, the intercepts are ½, ½, ½. The Miller indices

Fig. 3.17 A Model of an Important Reflecting Plane

This model represents a plane of atoms in a face-centered cubic metal. It can be imagined to pass through three corners of a cubic model in the manner of plane *abc* in Fig. 3.16. Because of the angle from which the plane was photographed the arrangement of atoms in the plane is not as clear as desirable. A better idea of how the atoms lie can be gained from Fig. 13.3 which shows a plane of identical character. A crystallographer calls a plane like this one a (111) plane.

are the reciprocals of these numbers. Therefore the plane has the Miller indices (222). The other plane in this drawing has intercepts a_o, a_o, and a_o or 1, 1, 1, of which the reciprocals, the Miller indices, are (111).

Suppose that a plane intercepts the x axis at a_o and the y axis at $a_o/2$ but is parallel to the z axis as shown in Drawing c of Fig. 3.18. Its intercepts may be written a_o, $a_o/2$, ∞.[4] Its Miller indices will be (120). A plane parallel to the yz plane of the coordinate system (the axes) and intersecting the x axis at a_o has the intercepts a_o, ∞, ∞ and the indices (100). A plane parallel to this one but intersecting the x axis at $a_o/2$ is a (200) plane. A plane parallel to the xy plane of the coordinate system and passing through $z = a_o$ is a (001) plane.

Planes may lie in many positions. One that has different intercepts on each of three axes is shown in Drawing d. Its indices are (234). Reasoning backwards, its intercepts can be deduced by taking the reciprocals of its indices. A plane similar to this one is also shown in the drawing. Planes may have one or more negative intercepts and indices. The one in drawing e intersects the negative end of the y axis and, accordingly, has the intercepts a_o, $-a_o$, $a_o/2$ as may be seen from the drawing. Its indices are ($1\bar{1}2$), the negative sign being put over the proper figure.

SOME GENERAL COMMENTS

A few general remarks may help to clarify some details for the reader.

(1) Drawings such as those in Fig. 3.18 show only the slope of the planes with respect to the selected axes. The planes actually extend to the boundaries of the crystal.

---

[4] ∞ is the symbol for infinity, that is, an indefinitely and incomprehensibly large number. Its use here is in agreement with the geometrical saying that "parallel planes meet at infinity." As the reciprocal of any very large number is a very small one, the reciprocal of ∞ must be 0.

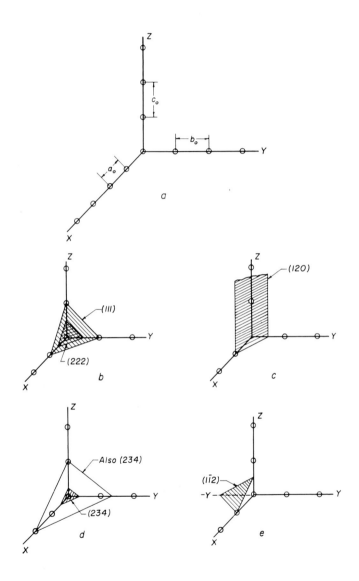

(2) When a type of plane such as (110) is specified, this statement should be understood as describing a whole set of equally spaced, parallel planes. The distance between planes is equal to the perpendicular distance from the origin to the first plane. The (220) planes are parallel to (110) planes but their spacing is only half as great.

(3) Planes with different indices may have identical arrangements of atoms. In a cubic metal like copper, a ($\bar{1}\bar{1}\bar{1}$) plane has the same appearance as a (111) plane. In fact, eight planes having the same arrangement of atoms on them but with different indices would be present.

(4) Reference is sometimes made to planes that have no physical existence. A line in a powder pattern may be indicated as having originated in a (400) plane whereas the crystal contains no such plane. What pro-

---

Fig. 3.18   The Planes in a Crystal

a. A set of mutually perpendicular axes with unit lengths marked off on each axis. Unit lengths correspond to the edges of unit cells, or equivalently, to lattice parameters. In this drawing, atoms are imagined to lie on each lattice point, a condition which often is not true. In the cubic system of crystals, a_o, b_o, and c_o all have the same value.

b. The (111) and (222) planes. These planes have similar atomic arrangements but lie at different distances from the origin. Each plane represents a whole set of parallel planes. The (111) planes are spaced twice as far apart as the (222) planes.

c. A plane parallel to an axis. The Miller index is zero for the axis to which the plane is parallel.

d. Two members of a set of (234) planes.

e. A plane with one negative intercept, and correspondingly, one negative index.

duced the line was a second order reflection from a (200) plane.

There are, of course, special meanings to other terms used by crystallographers.

REFERENCES

1. H. Mahl: "Orientierungsbestimmung von Aluminium-Einzelkristallen auf Uebermikroskopischem Wege," *Metallwirtschaft*, Vol. 19, 1940, p. 1082–1085.
2. M. J. Buerger: "X-Ray Crystallography," John Wiley & Sons, Inc., New York, 1942, Chapter 3.

CHAPTER 4

Alloys

IN THE PREVIOUS CHAPTERS, only unalloyed metals have been considered. This chapter will deal with some results obtained when two metals are alloyed. Actually, a metal almost always contains measurable amounts of other elements even after energetic efforts have been made to eliminate them. These alien elements may have been present in the ore from which the metal was extracted or may have been introduced during manufacturing operations. Such minor contaminants usually are not considered when alloying is under discussion.

SOLUBILITY OF METALS IN EACH OTHER

The combining of two metals in an alloying operation produces different behaviors according to the metals involved. The simplest behaviors occur either when the pairs of metals are completely immiscible in both the solid and the liquid state, or when they are completely miscible in both states.

Two metals that are completely immiscible in the liquid state—one may say that each is insoluble in the other—form two layers much as oil and water do. Even when the liquid metals have a limited solubility in each other, they still form two layers whenever the limiting solubilities are exceeded. Naturally, such alloys remain as two layers when they solidify. In most instances, such combinations are not of much interest but the characteristic of mutual insolubility may have a practical value, if one metal can be distributed throughout the other in the manner of an emulsion. Figure 4.1 shows a magnified radiograph of steel with particles of lead distributed through it. Because of the greater atomic weight of the

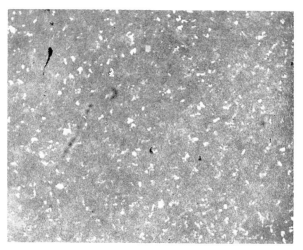

Fig. 4.1   Lead Particles in Low-Carbon Steel

Iron and lead do not alloy but the lead may be present in the iron as an assemblage of small particles. This picture is a magnified X-ray radiograph. Because the atoms of lead have a greater atomic weight than those of iron, they cut off, or absorb, more X-radiation; hence, the lead particles appear as white dots in the photograph.

Courtesy, Division of Metallurgy, National Bureau of Standards.   Magnification, 100×

lead atoms, the lead particles are less easily penetrated by X-rays than the matrix of iron in which they are distributed; hence, they show up as light spots. Lead[1] is sometimes added to steel to improve its machinability. When a leaded steel is being machined, for example, on a lathe or in an automatic screw machine, the chips break off at the lead particles instead of running out into long spirals.

Solid Solutions

Two metals that have complete mutual solubility in the liquid state behave much like water and alcohol; that is, the liquid alloy cannot be distinguished by appearance from a one-substance liquid. This resemblance to a single substance may exist in solid alloys also. For example, the iron-nickel alloy in Fig. 4.2 appears to be a single metal as far as one can determine by microscopic examination. One says that such an alloy is a *solid solution* because the two metals are mutually soluble in each other. Silver and gold are another pair of metals that are completely soluble in each other in both the solid and liquid states. Silver may be added to gold, or gold to silver, in any proportion, with little effect on the microscopic appearance of the solid alloy except for the change in color. Copper and nickel behave in the same way.

One should not assume, however, that the absence of any alteration in microscopic appearance means that no changes take place in such properties as electrical conductivity or magnetic susceptibility, or in the mechanical behavior. For example, an increase in strength is a common result of alloying and an important one. The hardening and strengthening of gold by the addi-

---

[1] As lead fumes are poisonous, some precautions are taken in heating lead-bearing steels so that the furnace operators will not be poisoned.

Fig. 4.2   An Alloy of Iron and Nickel

This alloy contains more than 50% nickel plus 4% molybdenum, yet microscopically, it cannot be distinguished from an unalloyed metal. Alloys like this one are called *solid solution* alloys.

Courtesy, E. E. Schumacher, Bell Telephone Laboratories, Inc.

Magnification, 200×

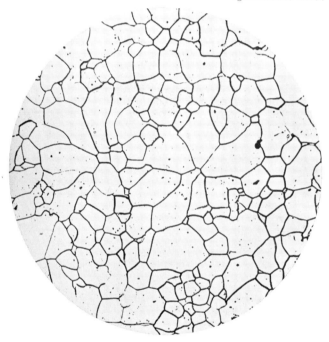

tion of silver or copper is a familiar fact. Advantage is taken of it by the jewelry manufacturers and also by the dental profession. Copper and nickel produce alloys which are much stronger than either of the component metals as will be observed by anyone who works with the copper-nickel alloy known as Monel metal.

HOW ATOMS ARE ARRANGED IN SOLID SOLUTIONS

We come now to the question of what happens on an atomic scale when two mutually soluble metals are alloyed, for example, when nickel is added to copper. One may imagine a crystal of copper in which the atoms are arranged like the balls in Fig. 3.8, and suppose that, by magic means, some atoms of copper are withdrawn and replaced by atoms of nickel. What will happen to the atomic arrangement? An important change is that the average distance between atoms will decrease because nickel atoms are slightly smaller than copper atoms. The decrease in average interatomic distance with increasing nickel content is shown in Fig. 4.3. One

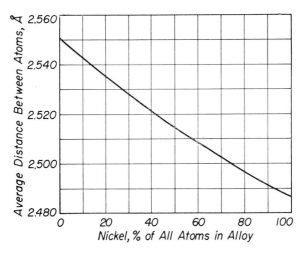

Fig. 4.3 Change of Interatomic Distance by Alloying

Because a nickel atom is smaller than a copper atom, the average distance between atoms decreases as nickel is added to copper (left). That the reverse effect takes place when copper is added to nickel is obvious from the right portion of the graph. This graph was drawn from data by Holgersson (*1*).

notes that the decrease is not strictly proportional to the percentage of nickel atoms added; otherwise, the graph would be a straight line.

The word *average* at the left in Fig. 4.3 should be noted. When two metals such as copper and nickel, or gold and silver, are alloyed, the two kinds of atoms appear to be mixed in a random, or accidental, distribution. Thus, to represent an alloy of 25% silver and 75% gold, one might assemble plain and gilded ping-pong balls in the ratio of 1 to 3 into a model similar to the one shown in Fig. 3.8 with the plain balls arranged by chance[2] among the gilded ones. Undoubtedly, the ratio of the two kinds of atoms in an alloy varies somewhat from one region to another and occasionally the variation will be considerable. Consequently, the distance between atoms will vary slightly from place to place in the alloy. For this reason, we say average distance.

So far, liquid alloys have been mentioned and some points have been noted about solid alloys but nothing has been said about the interesting process by which an alloy solidifies. As the detailed movements of atoms during solidification are not understood thoroughly, metallurgists usually describe the process in general terms. Also, solidification at practical rates almost always deviates in some details from the behavior assumed to be followed under the ideal conditions of very slow cooling and uniform temperature throughout the mass of metal. Hence, the customary explanation based on these favorable conditions idealizes the process.

The practice of idealizing a process is common in scientific and technical work and is the result of sheer necessity; the actual situation is so complicated as to defy analysis. To provide some workable theory, a sci-

---

[2] In special instances, the two kinds of atoms in an alloy are not mixed indiscriminately but have definite positions with respect to each other. Such an alloy is said to be "ordered."

entist may idealize a process; that is, he may set up a hypothetical situation that resembles the real one but is simple enough that he can make an analysis. Then, from this result he attempts to calculate what allowance should be made for his simplification and so arrive at the true result. Astronomers sometimes resort to this plan for certain calculations. Political propagandists frequently idealize situations to such a degree that their proposals have little value.

CONSTITUTIONAL DIAGRAMS

One of the important devices of metallurgical thought is the *constitutional diagram* which really is a graph that shows the temperature at which a change of some kind takes place in an alloy. A diagram for a series of alloys of only two metals is called a binary constitutional diagram. Figure 4.4 is the constitutional diagram for the copper-nickel alloys. The upper curved line gives the temperature of the beginning of solidification of an alloy containing the percentage (by weight) of nickel indicated along the base line. The lower curved line specifies the temperature at which solidification ends in an alloy containing the indicated percentage of nickel. Metallurgists call the upper line the *liquidus* line and the lower line the *solidus* line. Evidently, an alloy freezes over a range of temperature corresponding to the vertical distance between the curves rather than at a fixed temperature as copper and nickel do. For example, an alloy containing 50% nickel and 50% copper begins to solidify at about 1310°C. and is completely solid when it has cooled to about 1240°C. (Fig. 4.4).

HOW COPPER-NICKEL ALLOYS SOLIDIFY

The manner of solidification deserves a little more detailed examination. To study an alloy of 70% nickel and 30% copper we may take out the region near this composition from Fig. 4.4 and set it down as Fig. 4.5.

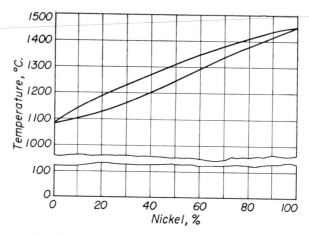

Fig. 4.4   The Nickel-Copper System of Alloys

The upper line gives the temperatures at which alloys begin to solidify and the lower one, the temperatures at which they are completely solid. In the reverse sense, the lower line gives the temperatures at which melting begins and the upper one, the temperatures at which melting is complete. Such a diagram is called a constitutional diagram. Hansen (2).

A line that may be called the *composition vertical* has been drawn at 70% nickel in the figure as a means of directing attention to the alloy concerned. The diagram shows that this alloy begins to solidify at 1375°C. and becomes solid at 1335°C.

A fact which may seem odd at first thought is that the first solid particle to form contains a higher percentage of nickel than the liquid in which it formed. Thus, when the cooling alloy reaches point *m*, the first bit to solidify contains about 80% nickel, point *n*. The higher nickel content of the solid portion must be at the expense of the liquid which now has an average nickel content of less than 70%. Because of its lower content of

Fig. 4.5 A Detail of the Nickel-Copper System

For the 70-30 alloy, m represents the temperature at which solidification begins, p gives the temperature at which the alloy is completely solid, n gives the composition of the first solid particle to form, and q gives the composition of the last trace of liquid as solidification nears completion.

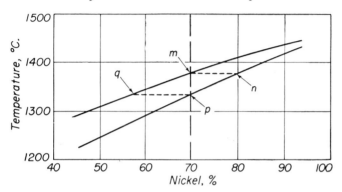

nickel, the solidifying temperature of the liquid is lowered. As cooling continues, the percentage of solid increases and the percentage of liquid decreases, but both solid and liquid become poorer in nickel until at the end of solidification, the solid p contains 70% nickel and the last trace of liquid q has only about 56%. It turns out that the composition of the liquid portion of the alloy at any temperature in the freezing range is given by the upper line and the composition of the solid portion, by the lower line. Thus, at 1350°C., the liquid contains 62% nickel and the solid 74%. Stated in another way, during solidification the composition of the liquid follows along the upper curve from m to q and the composition of the solid follows along the lower curve from n to p.

A diagram such as Fig. 4.4 or Fig. 4.5 also gives information concerning the melting process. Its lower line indicates for each composition the temperature at which melting begins. Likewise, its upper line tells when melting is complete. As one might suspect from a study of solidification, the first bit of molten material contains less nickel than the solid from which it came. Figure 4.5 shows that the first bit of liquid from the 70% alloy contains 56% nickel (point q). In general, melting may be considered as the reverse of solidification.

An interesting point arises when one considers the change in composition of the solid formed during solidification. Because the first solid to form contains 80% nickel and the last contains 70%, a logical first assumption is that the composition of the solid alloy varies from point to point. Yet the theory of constitutional diagrams is based on homogeneity of the solid. The missing fact is the diffusive action that takes place during solidification and immediately thereafter. Also, the time necessary for the diffusion of atoms is the basis for the requirement that solidification take place at an exceedingly slow rate.

In any practical case, the time necessary for diffusion is insufficient to yield a solid alloy that is homogeneous in composition. As a result the last portions to solidify have a lower solidification point (range) than the first portions. This condition can be demonstrated very easily since the regions with the lowest solidification point will also have the lowest melting point; hence, as the alloy is heated, the last regions to solidify will melt first. Figure 4.6 shows three stages in the melting of a rapidly solidified alloy containing about 70% nickel and 30% copper.

HOW ALLOYS MAY BE MADE HOMOGENEOUS

If the reader is in a state of discouragement about the possibility of obtaining a homogeneous alloy, this paragraph is intended to ease his mind. An alloy may be made sufficiently homogeneous for practical purposes if

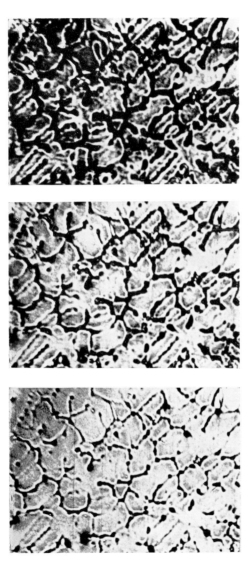

Fig. 4.6 The Melting of a Nickel-Copper Alloy

These three frames are from a motion picture taken at intervals during the melting of a nickel-copper alloy containing about 70% nickel. The early stage in liquefaction is at the left of the figure. The dark network in each frame represents metal that was molten at the time of that particular exposure. These dark areas were the ones that solidified last as the metal froze. They were adjacent to the grain boundaries.

Original magnification on film, 30×; magnification on print, 60×

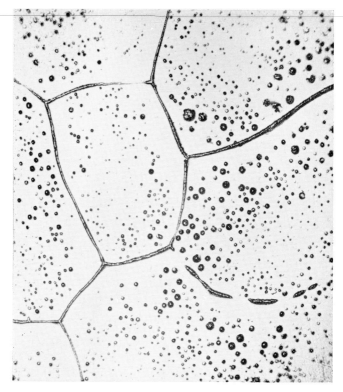

Fig. 4.7 An Iron-Manganese Alloy Beginning To Melt

This specimen was raised to a temperature so high that it
started to melt and was then cooled to room temperature.
The round dots indicate tiny regions that have been molten.
Evidence of melting is visible in the grain boundaries also.
The general distribution of the dots indicates the uniformity
of composition and the evenness of heating of the specimen.
Gayler (3).   Magnification, 150×

it is subjected to forging, rolling, or some other working or fabricating process and then reheated to a temperature somewhat below its melting point. The working and reheating may be repeated several times if desirable. Figure 4.7 illustrates how thoroughly homogeneous an alloy may be. It shows an iron-manganese alloy
that had been heated until melting started. As the composition was very nearly homogeneous, melting began
in a great many places at the same time as indicated by
the nearly uniform distribution of little dots and the
wide grain boundaries that result from incipient melting.

REFERENCES

1. Sven Holgersson: "Roentgenographische Strukturunter-
   suchungen von einigen Metallegierungen (Die Reihen
   AuAg und NiCu)," *Annalen der Physik*, Ser. 4, Vol. 79,
   1926, pp. 35–54.
2. M. Hansen: "Der Aufbau der Zweistofflegierungen," Julius
   Springer, Berlin, 1936. Photo-Lithoprint Reproduction
   by Edwards Brothers, Inc., Ann Arbor, Michigan, 1088
   p. (Constitutional diagrams in this book not otherwise
   credited have either been copied directly from or have
   been based on the diagrams in Hansen's book.)
3. Marie L. V. Gayler: "The Constitution of the Alloys of
   Iron and Manganese," *Journal*, The Iron and Steel Institute, Vol. 128, 1933, pp. 293–340.

CHAPTER 5

More About Alloys

From Fig. 4.4, one might assume that the combination of two metals with different melting points customarily yields an alloy having a melting temperature intermediate between those of the component metals. This assumption would not be correct because the effect of adding a small amount of a second metal more often is to lower the melting point of the first, regardless of their relative melting temperatures. As an illustration of this behavior, the lowering of the melting point of iron by the addition of molybdenum is shown graphically in Fig. 5.1. Iron melts at 1539°C. and molybdenum at 2610°C., yet the addition of molybdenum lowers the melting point of the alloy progressively until the molybdenum content exceeds 30%. Obviously, this trend does change eventually.

TIN-LEAD ALLOYS

Tin and lead behave toward each other much in the manner that molybdenum affects iron; that is, the addition of tin lowers the melting point of lead and vice

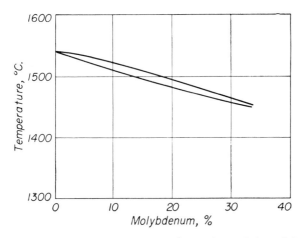

Fig. 5.1 Molybdenum Lowers the Melting Point of Iron

Molybdenum has a melting point above 2600°C. as compared with 1539°C. for iron, yet its addition produces an alloy with a lower melting point. The trend reverses at about 36% molybedenum. The upper line gives the temperature at which solidification begins and the lower line, the temperature at which it ends. This figure has been redrawn from Fig. 2 of Takei and Murakami (*1*).

versa. The tin-lead alloy system may well be described in some detail as it illustrates a relatively important class of alloy systems. Furthermore, the tin-lead alloys include the industrially valuable common solders. In a brief digression we may note that a frequently used common solder contains 40% tin and 60% lead, and, because of its composition, is called *forty-sixty* solder. Solder containing 50% of each metal, known as *fifty-fifty* or *half and half*, is also industrially important. Besides these alloys other combinations of tin and lead are used, including compositions having less than 40% and those

having more than 50% tin, as well as those within the
40 to 50% interval.

The constitutional diagram of the tin-lead alloy system is presented in Fig. 5.2. A glance suffices to indicate
how the two lines representing, respectively, the beginning and ending of solidification, fall toward lower temperatures as tin is added to lead, or lead to tin. In such
a diagram, one still calls the upper line, *ABC,* the liquidus line and the lower line, *ADBEC,* the solidus line.

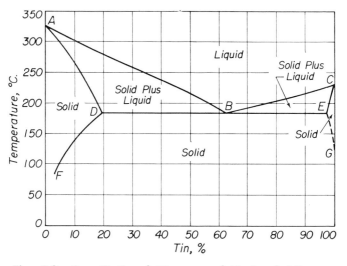

Fig. 5.2   Constitutional Diagram of Tin-Lead Alloys

The upper broken line, *ABC,* represents the temperatures at
which molten alloys begin to solidify and the lower line,
ADBEC, represents the temperatures at which they are solid.
For example, the alloy with 10% tin begins to solidify at about
300°C. and is completely solid at about 270°C. In the reverse
order, the lines indicate when the solid alloy begins to melt
and when it finishes melting. This diagram gives the melting
and solidifying temperatures of all possible compositions of
alloys of the two component metals. The significance of the
lines *DF* and *EG* will be considered in Chapter 8.

This figure arouses the suspicion that the lead-tin alloys may not behave like the copper-nickel alloys when they undergo solidification. This suspicion appears justified if one observes the inhomogeneity of the polished section of the 45% tin-55% lead alloy in Fig. 5.3. The analysis given below shows that although alloys con-

---

Fig. 5.3   Microscopic Appearance of Tin-Lead Solder

This specimen contained about 45% tin. The dark areas are mainly lead but contain some tin. The striated areas that surround the dark islands represent alternate layers of lead (dark) and tin (light). This solder was cooled more slowly than is customary in soldering operations.

Magnification, 100×

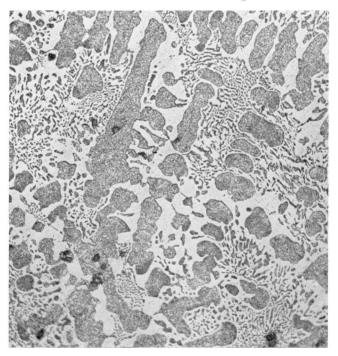

taining less than 19.5% tin (compositions to the left of *D*) or more than 97.5% tin (to the right of *E*) resemble the copper-nickel alloys in their manner of solidification, those in between do, indeed, solidify in a different manner. The effect of composition on the process of freezing may be illustrated by descriptions of the solidification of two alloys containing, respectively, 8% and 45% tin.

THE 8% TIN ALLOY

How closely the solidification of an 8% tin alloy resembles the same process in the copper-nickel alloys may be observed from the following description. When the 8% alloy cools to 305°C., point *m* in Fig. 5.4, particles of solid begin to form; they have the composition 3.7% tin and 96.3% lead, point *n*. As cooling continues, the liquid portion of the alloy decreases in amount but increases in tin content. During this period, the temperature and composition of the liquid are represented by a succession of points along *AB* from *m* to *q*. While these changes are proceeding, the solid portion increases in amount and in tin content. Its temperature and composition are represented by a succession of points along *AD* from *n* to *p*.

What the above paragraph has implied is that the compositions of both solid and liquid are known for each temperature in the freezing range. It has implied, also, that both solid and liquid actually are at the same temperature. Equality of temperature obviously is a justifiable assumption because the two portions are in intimate contact and, for reasonably slow cooling, the flow of heat from one to the other equalizes their temperatures. From this information, one concludes that for any horizontal line connecting curves *AD* and *AB*, the points of intersection of that line with the curves give the compositions for that particular temperature. Thus, at 300°C., the solid contains 4% tin and the liquid, 10.5% tin.

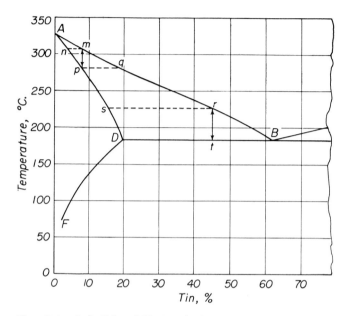

Fig. 5.4   Left Side of Tin-Lead Diagram

Other lines have been added as aids in the description of the solidification of two representative alloys.

The 8% tin alloy completes the solidifying process at point p, 282°C. The composition of the last liquid to freeze is indicated by q, about 18.5% tin. As the alloy continues to cool after solidification, its composition must remain at 8% tin. Correspondingly, the points that represent it on the diagram follow down a vertical line at 8% tin. No change takes place in the chemical character of the alloy, a solid solution, until the temperature has decreased to about 140°C. That something must happen then is indicated by the existence of the line DF. What it is that happens is explained in Chapter 8.

THE LAW OF LEVERS

Not only can the compositions be determined if the temperature is known but also the relative amounts of solid and liquid. This information is obtained from a very simple relationship known as the "Law of Levers." This law is not difficult to derive but the calculations that it permits may be understood most easily from an illustration. Suppose that an alloy containing 30% tin has cooled to 227°C., line sr in Fig. 5.4. Then according to this figure, the composition of the solid is s, 15.5% tin and of the liquid, r, 45% tin. What the law of levers says is that if the composition of the whole alloy, 30% tin, be considered as a fulcrum, the weight of the liquid times its lever arm $(r - 30)$ equals the weight of solid times its lever arm $(30 - s)$. The more common way of stating this relationship is

$$\frac{\text{weight of liquid}}{\text{weight of solid}} = \frac{30 - s}{r - 30} = \frac{30 - 15.5}{45 - 30} = 0.965$$

that is, the alloy is a little less than 50% liquid and a little more than 50% solid. At 200°C., the ratio of liquid to solid is

$$\frac{\text{weight of liquid}}{\text{weight of solid}} = \frac{30 - 18}{56 - 30} = 0.46$$

These calculations show that there is much less liquid at 200°C. than at 227°C., a result which was to be expected.

If one wants to state the amount of liquid at 200°C. as a percentage of the weight of the entire mass of alloy (liquid plus solid) the corresponding relationship is, for 200°C.,

$$\frac{\text{weight of liquid}}{\text{weight of alloy}} \times 100 = \frac{30 - 18}{56 - 18} \times 100 = 31.5\%$$

Evidently, the law of levers as applied to a freezing alloy of metals X and Y may be expressed in either of two forms:

$$\frac{\text{weight of liquid}}{\text{weight of solid}} = \frac{\%\text{ of }Y\text{ in alloy} - \%\text{ of }Y\text{ in solid}}{\%\text{ of }Y\text{ in liquid} - \%\text{ of }Y\text{ in alloy}}$$

or,

$$\%\text{ of alloy that is liquid} = \frac{\%\text{ of }Y\text{ in alloy} - \%\text{ of }Y\text{ in solid}}{\%\text{ of }Y\text{ in liquid} - \%\text{ of }Y\text{ in solid}} \times 100$$

These expressions hold also for alloys to the right of B although in this range, both numerator and denominator calculate out to be negative if the composition is still expressed in $\%$ of Y.

THE 45% TIN ALLOY

The 45% alloy may be taken as representative of alloys from 19.5% to 62% tin, point D to point B. Actually it illustrates equally well the behavior of alloys from 62% to 97.5% tin. Solidification of the 45% alloy begins at $227°C.$, point r, by the precipitation (formation) of solid containing 15.5% tin, point s. During further cooling, both the solid and the liquid portions increase in tin content just as they did in the 8% alloy. However, when the temperature has decreased to $183°C.$, the alloy is still more than half liquid as becomes evident if one calculates the ratio of liquid to solid; the ratio of liquid to solid is equal to the length Dt (or $t - D$) divided by length tB (or $B - t$). This liquid, which contains 62% tin, freezes completely at $183°C.$ to a composite solid consisting mainly of alternate irregular plates of lead and tin.[1] The solidified alloy as a whole,

---

[1] It is convenient to refer to these laminae as alternate lead and tin plates. Actually, the "lead" and "tin" plates are "lead-rich" and "tin-rich" plates. The lead-rich plates contain 19.5% tin and the tin-rich plates contain 2.5% lead corresponding to points D and E of Fig. 5.2, respectively.

consists of solid masses, or islands, rich in lead that
formed during cooling from 227°C. to 183°C. which are
surrounded by the striated regions that resulted from the
solidification of all of the liquid that existed at 183°C.
This is the alloy pictured in Fig. 5.3.

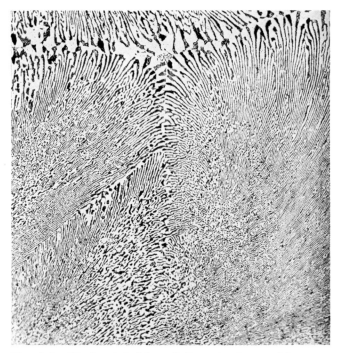

Fig. 5.5   Tin-Lead Solder of Eutectic Composition

A polished and etched cross section of tin-lead solder containing 62% tin shows no lead islands. Instead, the entire
alloy is composed of alternate layers, or laminae, of lead and
tin. (The lead contains some tin and the tin contains some
lead.) Structures of this kind are called eutectic structures because they occur when the composition of the alloy has eutectic, or lowest melting, proportions.

Magnification, 75×

If one were to imagine photomicrographs of a series of alloys as they exist immediately below 183°C., he would think first of those from 0 to 19.5% tin. They would all show a single, microscopically homogeneous substance—a solid solution of tin in lead.[2] As the tin content increased, an area of alternate tin and lead bands would appear. With further addition of tin, the striated regions would increase in area relatively to the area of islands until, at 45% tin, the polished and etched specimens would resemble Fig. 5.3. When the tin content reached 62%, the alloy would appear as in Fig. 5.5, the area of lead-rich islands having diminished to the vanishing point. As the tin content increased above 62%, islands of tin-rich constituent would increase in area until at 97.5% tin, the alloy would consist entirely of a homogeneous tin-rich solid solution.

Alloy of composition B (Fig. 5.2) obviously has the lowest melting—and freezing—temperature of any alloy in the lead-tin system. Furthermore, as the diagram indicates, it solidifies or melts at a fixed temperature just as truly as an unalloyed metal does. It is called the "eutectic" alloy from a Greek word meaning easy melting. Other alloy systems also have eutectic alloys and their existence is indicated in their constitutional diagrams by a configuration of lines like that in the vicinity of B. Because alloys of "eutectic composition" very often solidify into an assemblage of alternate plates like those in Fig. 5.5, these lamellar structures[3] usually are

---

[2] This statement is based on the ideal condition that cooling through solidification is sufficiently slow to permit complete diffusion to take place. For ordinary rates of cooling, the presence of laminated structure is likely to become evident for tin contents below 19.5%. As a practical matter, photomicrographs would be taken of alloys at room temperature. The alloys would be quenched very rapidly, then polished, etched, and photographed at room temperature. Quenching, if sufficiently rapid, probably would hold the alloy in about the condition in which it existed just below 183°C.

[3] Although eutectic structures actually are composed of alternate plates, one sees only cross sections of the plates in the microscopic section.

called "eutectic structures." The term "eutectic temperature" is also used.

THE MELTING PROCESS

If one could look inside a metal, he undoubtedly
could get a clearer idea of what goes on during solidification or melting. Unfortunately, devices for looking
into a metal are limited in performance. However, it
is possible to watch the melting of a metal or alloy in a
tiny furnace placed under a microscope objective. Figure 5.6 shows four frames of a motion picture film depicting the melting of a cadmium-bismuth alloy. The
white portions indicate the regions that froze first as the
metal cooled; they correspond to the dark islands of
lead in Fig. 5.3. The dark portions are poorly defined
eutectic that formed when the remaining liquid reached
the eutectic composition, 57% bismuth, and froze at the
eutectic temperature, 144°C. Examination of the figure
reveals that the eutectic region melts first and then, as
the temperature rises, the white crystals of cadmium
melt gradually. Unlike the tin-lead alloys, cadmium
and bismuth appear to have very little solid solubility
for each other; that is, cadmium will not allow a meas-

Fig. 5.6 Melting of a Cadmium-Bismuth Alloy

The first frame, taken from a motion picture of the melting
of the alloy, shows the islands of cadmium surrounded b
poorly formed eutectic that is beginning to melt. In the secone
frame, most of the eutectic area is already molten and th
islands are beginning to melt. If the temperature had bee
the same over the entire specimen—the temperature of th
furnace was very far from uniform—all of the eutectic woul
have melted before detectable melting of the islands occurred
Remaining frames depict the melting of the primary grain
(islands) of cadmium.

Final magnification, 60>

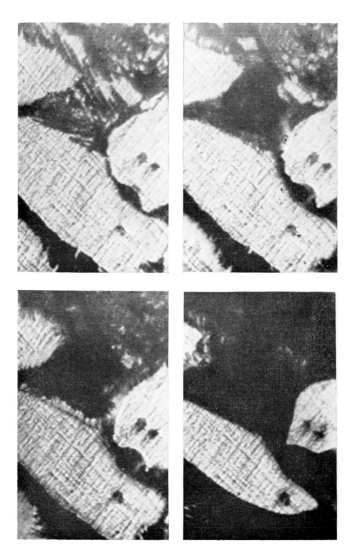

urable number of bismuth atoms to replace its own atoms, nor will bismuth allow any cadmium atoms to enter its structure. This fact is made apparent in the constitutional diagram, Fig. 5.7, by the absence of lines corresponding to *ADF* and *CEG* of the tin-lead diagram. The points *D* and *E* may be imagined to have moved to the left and right, respectively, and to have disappeared into the border lines of the diagram.

FACTORS THAT INFLUENCE ALLOYING—ATOMIC DIAMETER

If some rules could be established for predicting what kind of an alloy two metals would form, the difficulty of finding the best combination would be lessened. Unfortunately, no satisfactory rules are available yet. However, a few general observations have been made.

Many valuable alloys are of the solid solution type. Examples are stainless steel and Monel metal. Brasses

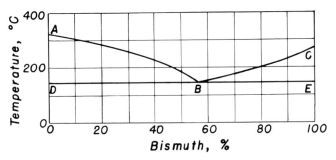

Fig. 5.7   Bismuth-Cadmium Diagram

This diagram has a similarity to the constitutional diagrams of Fig. 5.2 and Fig. 5.8. Because neither metal has a measurable solubility in the other, the regions of solid solubility corresponding to areas α and β in Fig. 5.8 have shrunk to zero dimensions and vanished. Accordingly, the lines *ADF* and *CEG* that appear in Fig. 5.2 and Fig. 5.8 have receded into the side boundaries of the diagram.

and bronzes are solid solutions over their most useful ranges of composition. As described in the previous chapter, a solid solution is the kind of a product one would expect to get if he could replace some of the atoms of metal *A* with atoms of metal *B* without changing the structure otherwise. If the two kinds of atoms are nearly the same size, such substitution might seem

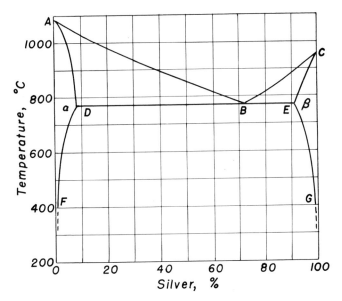

Fig. 5.8 Constitutional Diagram of the Copper-Silver Alloys

This diagram is of the same general type as the lead-tin diagram. It shows that copper will not take into solid solution more than 8.0% silver and that silver will not take more than 8.8% copper into solid solution. In fact, only at the eutectic temperature can these amounts be held in solid solution. The solubility decreases with temperature, a fact that is indicated by the curving lines *DF* and *EG*.

to present relatively little difficulty. The evidence confirms this belief in a general way. For example, copper and nickel, which differ by about 2.5% in the diameters of their atoms, were shown in Chapter 4 to form a solid solution at all proportions. Metals that behave in this manner may be described as having "diagram-wide" solid solubility.

Two metals may exhibit diagram-wide solid solubility for differences in atomic diameter considerably larger than 2.5%. For example, the diameters of gold and copper atoms differ by about 12% but the two metals have complete mutual solid solubility. On the other hand, copper and silver also have about 12% difference in the diameter of their atoms but their mutual solubility is limited as shown in Fig. 5.8 to about 8.0% silver in copper and about 8.8% copper in silver. As soon as the content of one metal in the other exceeds these limits, an eutectic structure begins to form as shown in Fig. 5.9. In this instance, the silver content of the alloy was a little more than the 8% that copper can take into solid solution. A fact to be noted is that these maximum solubilities of 8.0% and 8.8% refer to the eutectic temperature, about 779°C. The solubility of either metal in the other is much less at room temperature as the curving lines bounding the solid solution areas α and β indicate. Evidently, other factors than relative size of atoms have a strong influence.[4] However, relative size does appear to impose a limit even when other factors are favorable. If the difference in atomic diameter exceeds 14% or 15%, solid solubility is highly restricted.

---

[4] Some typical diameters of atoms expressed in Ångstrom units are:

chromium	—	2.493	molybdenum	—	2.720
columbium	—	2.853	nickel	—	2.486
copper	—	2.551	silver	—	2.882
gold	—	2.878	tin	—	3.016
iron	—	2.476	zinc	—	2.659
lead	—	3.493			

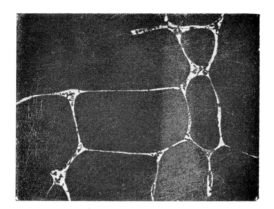

Fig. 5.9   Excess Silver Beyond Solubility Limit

This photomicrograph shows a copper-silver alloy in which the content of silver exceeds slightly the proportion that will go into solid solution in copper. As a result, a small amount of copper-silver eutectic has formed. A point to be noted is that the silver present in the eutectic contains about 8.8% copper in solid solution.

Phillips and Brick (2).   Magnification, 100×

FACTORS THAT INFLUENCE ALLOYING—CHEMICAL PROPERTIES

The manner in which two metals alloy depends also upon their chemical character. If they have the same chemical valence, and in particular, if they appear in the same column of the periodic table (Fig. 1.1) they are likely to have a considerable mutual solid solubility. This statement holds especially for metals in columns 4 to 11 in the table. On the other hand, if the two metals are from opposite sides of the periodic table, they are likely to form compounds rather than solid solutions. For example, magnesium and lead form a compound with the formula Mg₂Pb. The diagram of the magnesium-lead system, appearing as Fig. 5.10, is divided by this compound into two sections each of which is eutectic in character.

Intermetallic compounds vary widely in their nature and properties. In many of them customary ideas of

---

Fig. 5.10 Magnesium-Lead Diagram

These metals form a compound Mg_2Pb when the proportions present are 80.99% lead and 19.01% magnesium, composition L. This compound has the effect of splitting the diagram into two parts at the line $CGHL$ with the result that two eutectics occur. The compound is present in all solid alloys between the lines FK and JM. Only traces are present at these lines but the entire alloy consists of compound at L. Recent work shows that the magnesium-lead diagram actually is more complex than is indicated by the figure but the statements above are still correct.

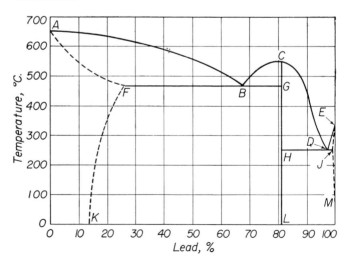

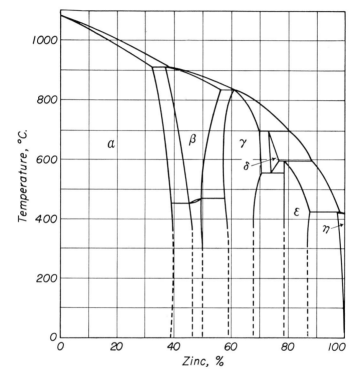

Fig. 5.11 Copper-Zinc System

This constitutional diagram is introduced mainly to illustrate
the complexity which some alloy systems possess. Alloys up to
about 40% zinc are known commercially as *alpha* brass; the
name is given to them because their composition falls in the
area below 40% zinc, which is marked with the Greek letter
alpha. The marking of different areas in a constitutional
diagram with Greek letters is a common practice.

chemical valence are violated. The potassium-sodium compound, KNa$_2$, is an example. Compounds of this type frequently dissociate instead of melting when they are heated. The subject of chemical effects is extensive. Interested readers should study books that deal especially with it such as the one by Hume-Rothery (3).

SOME GENERAL REMARKS ON DIAGRAMS

A point that has yet to be made is that for complete, or diagram-wide solid solubility, the two metals must have the same kind of unit cells or space lattices. A face-centered cubic metal and a close-packed hexagonal metal cannot form a system of alloys with complete mutual solid solubility even if their atoms are exactly the same size.

A characteristic feature of alloy (constitutional) diagrams in which solid solubility is diagram-wide is that the liquidus and solidus curves run smoothly from one side of the diagram to the other. The curves do not necessarily climb from one side to the other as in the copper-nickel diagram. They may pass through a minimum as in the copper-gold alloys. In such a system, both liquidus and solidus curves must pass through their minimum values at the same composition and must touch at that composition while retaining their smooth curvatures.

Alloy diagrams may be very complex. One that is moderately so is the copper-zinc diagram in Fig. 5.11. The alloys that have zinc contents below about 39% are called alpha brasses in accordance with the alpha in the area at the left of this diagram. One speaks also of beta brasses and, occasionally, of gamma brasses.

REFERENCES

1. Takeshi Takei and Takejiro Murakami: "On the Equilibrium Diagram of the Iron-Molybdenum System," *Trans-*

   actions, American Society for Steel Treating, Vol. 16, 1929, pp. 339–358.

2. Arthur Phillips and R. M. Brick: "Segregation in Single Crystals of Solid Solution Alloys," *Transactions,* American Institute of Mining and Metallurgical Engineers, Vol. 124, 1937, pp. 313–329.

3. William Hume-Rothery: "Atomic Theory for Students of Metallurgy," 1960 edition, Institute of Metals, London.

CHAPTER 6

Solidification

THIS CHAPTER covers several topics related to the solidification of metals. Because it has something of the nature of a miscellany, a list of the subjects in it may be useful. They are the following:

1. The tendency of solidifying particles to grow in definite crystallographic directions.
2. The effect of flow of heat on the orientation, or position in space, of metallic crystals.
3. The effect of rapid cooling on the uniformity of composition and on the structure of alloys.
4. The production of large single crystals.

CRYSTALS GROW IN PARTICULAR DIRECTIONS

A factor that is important at all rates of cooling is the tendency of the atoms in a cooling liquid to attach themselves in a particular way to existing solid nuclei. As a result of this behavior, rapid growth occurs in particular crystallographic directions. For example, a metal of the face-centered cubic type grows most rapidly in directions that correspond to the edges of the model in

Fig. 3.8, equivalently, to the edges of the corresponding unit cell. This characteristic was observed many years ago and one of the early metallurgists made a drawing to illustrate a growing crystal. His illustration is reproduced here as Fig. 6.1.

Fig. 6.1   Idealized Crystal of Metal

This idealized drawing represents the kind of crystals formed during solidification of metals of the cubic systems. Because of its resemblance to a tree, the crystal is called a *dendrite*.

A crystal of a face-centered cubic or body-centered cubic metal extends out in three directions corresponding to the perpendiculars to the faces of a cube. The extent to which this crystal has been idealized will be understood if this figure is compared with the next one.

Tschernoff.

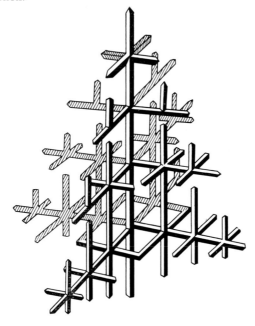

The evidence for growth in favored directions has been derived from a number of sources. An example is the microscopic structure observed in alloys in which a solid solution forms first and a eutectic substance afterwards. The 45% tin lead-tin alloy solidified in this way. A slightly better illustration of the tendency of the solidifying metal to grow in definite directions appears in Fig. 6.2 which shows primary grains with surrounding eutectic material in an aluminum-silicon alloy. One notes in this figure that the white material, the primary crystals, bears some resemblance to a tree. For this rea-

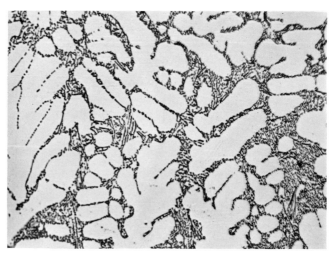

Fig. 6.2   Directional Growth of Primary Crystals in an Aluminum-Silicon Alloy

This alloy was cooled too rapidly for the proper development of good directional growth but the tendency for such growth is evident. Some resemblance to the form of a pine tree is evident.

Plumb and Lewis (*1*).   Magnification, 500×

son, structures of this kind are called "dendrites." Dendrite is a modified form of a Greek word for tree.

The tendency of a crystal to grow in specific crystallographic directions exists, likewise, in alloys of solid solution type and, as shown in a later section of this chapter, it becomes apparent for rapid rates of cooling. Dendritic growth is the normal way of solidification in unalloyed metals, also. It is not usually detected under the microscope, however, because the finally solidified metal has a uniform composition and, consequently, etching reagents act uniformly on it. That growth does take place in favored directions was evident in the picture of bismuth in Fig. 3.2. In this example, the shapes of bismuth crystals left after the liquid metal was poured off reveal clearly the rapid growth in specific directions. Examples of treelike forms are found occasionally in commercial operations. They occur in ingots or castings in which, because of shrinkage, liquid has drained away from a partly grown crystal.

FLOW OF HEAT INFLUENCES CRYSTAL GROWTH

An interesting observation is that crystals in a freezing metal tend to orient themselves with respect to the direction in which heat is flowing. Whether the original nuclei have this orientation or whether only those nuclei so oriented grow rapidly is difficult to determine but the resulting crystals have a strong preference for particular positions. Examples of this type of behavior are common in ingots. In many instances, long columnar crystals extend out from the walls of the mold as depicted in Fig. 6.3. They seem to have grown against the current of heat flowing from the center of the molten mass toward the mold wall. If the metal in the mold has a face-centered cubic structure when solid, the orientation of the columnar grains is about what it would be if the bottom of the model in Fig. 3.8 were placed against the wall. The grains grow in a direction corresponding to the vertical in the original position of the model. A crystallographer would say that a (100) plane is against the wall and that the crystal grows in the [001] direction.

The growth of large crystals occurs most readily in metals that have only a low content of other elements. Bismuth crystals like those pictured in Fig. 3.2 develop only in "pure" metal. Certainly, very small percentages of contaminating elements destroy the capacity of some metals to form large crystals. Copper that has not been treated for removal of oxygen does not produce long columnar crystals like those in Fig. 6.3. Ingots of ordinary copper have columnar grains near the walls but their interior regions are equiaxed, that is, the grains have roughly the same dimensions in all directions. The change in character of the grains as the zone of solidification moves inward from the walls toward the center takes place in a relatively short distance. A possible explanation of it is that the oxygen rejected from the first metal to solidify, the columnar grains, has moved toward the center and at the point of change has a concentration sufficient to alter the manner of solidification. Steel ingots frequently have a region of small equiaxed grains on the outside, then a wide zone of columnar grains, and, in the interior, another region of equiaxed grains. The process of solidification of such ingots is relatively complex.

EFFECT OF RAPID COOLING ON ALLOYS

In previous chapters, solidification was described as proceeding at a rate so slow that diffusion of atoms could maintain uniformity of composition not only in the liquid but in the solid also. Solidification in this manner is specified as taking place under "equilibrium" conditions. Even in a laboratory these ideal conditions are difficult to establish. In commercial operations, cooling

Fig. 6.3 Cross Section of a Copper Ingot

The ingot is a vertically cast wire bar of OFHC (oxygen-free, high-conductivity) copper. It contains less oxygen than the bars from which wire usually is drawn. Copper containing the customary amount of oxygen will not produce such long columnar grains as these. Solidification began at the outside where the copper was in contact with the comparatively cool mold.

Courtesy, H. M. Schleicher, The American Metal Co., Ltd.

⅞ actual size

usually is relatively rapid and, hence, faster than an equilibrium rate. Unalloyed metals are affected comparatively little by rate of cooling but if an alloy solidifies rapidly, its composition may be far from uniform. Figure 6.4 shows an example of nonuniformity in brass of the 70% copper-30% zinc type, often called cartridge brass. According to the copper-zinc diagram of Fig. 5.11, brass containing less than 33% zinc should freeze into an alpha solid solution if it is cooled under equilibrium conditions. Hence, its composition should be uniform and it should appear uniform in a polished and etched section. Evidently this specimen did not solidify under equilibrium conditions.

What has happened to cause the peculiar appearance of Fig. 6.4 is not difficult to imagine. Skeletal, or dendritic, type crystals were formed during the initial freezing period. These skeletons, the trunks and branches of the dendrites, must be considerably richer in copper than the alloy as a whole according to the analysis of freezing in the copper-nickel system, which is applicable in this instance, also. Because so little time was available for diffusion, they remained rich in copper even during the later stages of solidification. Hence, the last portions of the alloy to solidify must have abnormally low copper content. As the etching reagent reacted on the surface according to the copper content at any point, it brought out the dendritic nature of the piece. Nonuniformity of this kind frequently is called "coring."

THE CORRECTION OF NONUNIFORMITY OF COMPOSITION

As pointed out in Chapter 4, an inhomogeneous alloy may be made more nearly uniform in structure and composition by alternate working (deformation) and heating. If the piece is a casting intended for use in the form in which it was cast, such treatment is not permissible. A useful improvement of structure can be pro-

Fig. 6.4   Coring in Cast 70–30 Brass

In the two dark grains, the copper-rich trunks and branches of the dendritic crystals show a lighter color after etching than the less rich outer portions. The same situation prevails in the light grain but is less striking. This nonuniformity of composition is the result of incomplete diffusion of the atoms of the component metals during freezing.

Courtesy, D. K. Crampton, Chase Brass & Copper Co.

Magnification, 150×

duced, however, if the casting is held for a long time at a relatively high temperature. This treatment allows a degree of diffusion that alleviates the nonuniform condition. The highest temperature that may be used in the treatment sometimes is limited by a tendency of the piece to warp.

What appears to be a contradictory proceeding is intentionally rapid cooling during solidification. Such a practice may actually be beneficial at times because it reduces large-scale segregation that results from circulation of molten metal in the incompletely solidified ingot or casting.

SINGLE CRYSTALS

An interesting method is used in laboratories to produce small ingots of metal which are composed of only a few crystals, or perhaps only one large crystal. The apparatus for making such ingots is illustrated in Fig. 6.5. The cylindrical crucible A with a pointed bottom may be lowered out of the heating element B at a controlled rate. Solidification begins when the metal at the tip cools to the freezing point and continues upward in the descending crucible but always at about the same position with respect to heating element B. The figure shows the crucible about halfway out of the heating element. Several columnar grains are in process of growing but the upper portion of the charge is still liquid.

One can imagine how the solidification takes place in crucible A. As the atoms in the tip cool to the solidifying temperature, they arrange themselves into a nucleus of solid metal (giving up some freedom of motion with resultant evolution of heat); then more atoms from the liquid attach themselves to the nucleus as the crucible descends and so form a columnar crystal. In some instances, no other nucleus forms and the entire mass of metal is converted into a single crystal. In others, one or more additional nuclei do form, perhaps by chance, perhaps because of some slight local cooling, or because

Fig. 6.5 Apparatus for Making Single Crystals

The crucible A is lowered slowly from the heating element B so that the metal in the tip solidifies first. In some experiments, the entire ingot is composed entirely of a single crystal. In others, two or more crystals may form as the metal solidifies. This method of making single crystals was developed by Professor Bridgman (2).

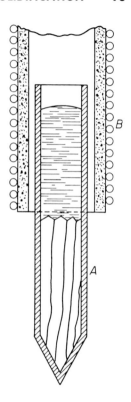

a minute impurity offered a good surface to which atoms from the liquid could attach themselves, with a result something like that depicted in Fig. 6.5.

REFERENCES

1. R. C. Plumb and J. E. Lewis: "The Modification of Aluminium-Silicon Alloys by Sodium," *Journal,* Institute of Metals, Vol. 86, 1957–58, pp. 393–400.
2. P. W. Bridgman: "The Compressibility of Thirty Metals as a Function of Pressure and Temperature," *Proceedings*, American Academy of Science, Vol. 58, 1923, pp. 165–242.

CHAPTER 7

Movement of Atoms in Solid Metals

ONE WOULD THINK that after it had solidfied a metal would be less subject to alteration than the laws of the Medes and the Persians. Nothing among human surroundings appears more fixed in its nature than a metal, yet abundant evidence exists that the atoms in metals are in more or less continuous motion even at temperatures far below their melting points. Many experiments indicate travel through distances that mean movement past thousands of other atoms.

Actually, metallurgical operations based on the movement of atoms have been practiced for many years. They include processes for hardening the surfaces of metals of which one example is the old art of case-hardening steel. Also, some methods for increasing the resistance to corrosion of the underlying metal depend upon surface layers obtained by diffusion. Serious study of the movements of atoms has been undertaken only during the present century.

AN EXAMPLE OF THE MOVEMENT OF ATOMS

Many cases of atomic migration have been studied because of a desire to understand the reason for some unanticipated, and often undesirable, effect. However, one of the early investigations was a matter of satisfying curiosity. Roberts-Austen (*1*), who was director of the British mint, clamped together two well-cleaned blocks, one of gold and one of lead, and allowed them to remain in contact for four years. Analyses made at the end of that period showed that gold could be detected in the lead block as far as ⁵⁄₁₆ inch from the interface.

MOVEMENT OF COPPER ATOMS IN ALUMINUM

One practical effect of the migratory movement of atoms has been observed in duplex aluminum products. Aluminum can be hardened and strengthened greatly by the addition of other elements; for example, the ultimate tensile strength can be raised from 20,000 to 70,000 psi (pounds per square inch) or even higher. Unfortunately, these added elements sometimes make the metal less resistant to corrosive influences such as chemicals or salty atmospheres. As a counter-measure, manufacturers cover the strong, alloyed material with a thin layer of unalloyed aluminum or sometimes of another aluminum alloy that itself has a good resistance to corrosion. This procedure gives excellent results but if the temperature of the duplex sheet is accidentally raised too high in some fabricating operation, alloying elements may migrate from the base sheet into the unalloyed coating. If the migration continues until the alloying atoms reach the surface of the coating, the result will be a reduced resistance to corrosion of the protecting sheet.

Figures 7.1a and 7.1b illustrate the movement of copper from an aluminum-copper alloy base sheet into a protective coating of unalloyed aluminum as the result of excessive temperature. The reagent used for etching these specimens was of a type that did not color unalloyed aluminum but darkened aluminum that contained copper. Figure 7.1a indicates that the atoms migrate most rapidly along grain boundaries as the grains have been darkened adjacent to the boundaries but not in the interior. When the duplex piece was held for a longer period at the elevated temperature, the copper atoms diffused through the interior regions also as shown in Fig. 7.1b.

Fig. 7.1a Copper Diffusing Through Grain Boundaries of Aluminum Sheet

Outer surface of a sheet that was heated while in intimate contact with an underlying sheet of copper-bearing alloy. Copper diffused upward through the grain boundaries and caused them to appear as dark, wide lines when etched. The unalloyed interiors of the grains were not affected by etching. Evidently, diffusion is more rapid through the boundaries than through the interior of the grains.

Keller and Brown (2).

Magnification, 85×

Fig. 7.1b Copper Coming Through Interior of Grains After Longer Heating

DIFFUSION HOMOGENIZES ALLOYS

Suppose disks of two different metals, *A* and *B,* are clamped together tightly. If the bond between them is sufficiently adherent, one can consider the assembly to be a single piece of metal, that is, an alloy of extremely nonuniform composition. Consequently, in accordance with the tendency of alloys to become more homogeneous with time, atoms of *A* would begin to move into *B* and atoms of *B* into *A*. For a pair of metals like copper and nickel,[1] one can get an idea of the rate at which the assembly becomes homogeneous by a study of Fig. 7.2. This figure shows the state of affairs in the assembly after 312 hours at 1054°C. In that time, nickel atoms have penetrated into the copper—which is on the right side of the zero vertical—to a distance of about 1 millimeter. During the same time, the copper atoms have penetrated into the nickel disk only about half that far. That is, the nickel disk is still unalloyed nickel beyond about 0.6 millimeter from the joining plane.

From the rates of diffusion suggested by Fig. 7.2, two deductions can be made. One is that even at the relatively high temperature of 1054°C., 30°C. below the melting point of copper, a very long time must elapse before the assembly will become reasonably homogeneous. The other is related to the process of solidification. The observed slowness of diffusion means that extremely slow cooling must prevail if the solid portion is to have sufficient time to become homogeneous. This statement will be true even though the rate of atomic movement increases rapidly as the temperature is raised.

---

[1] Copper and nickel make a good combination for illustration because of their diagram-wide solid solubility as described in previous chapters. If the two metals have only a limited solubility for each other—for example, if *A* can take up only 3% of *B* and *B* can take up only 5% of *A*—the final situation becomes a little more complicated.

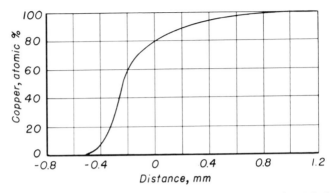

Fig. 7.2   Diffusion of Copper Into Nickel and Nickel Into Copper

Disks of copper and nickel were welded together and then heated at 1054°C. for 312 hours. As the figure shows, nickel penetrated into copper about 1 mm. and copper penetrated into nickel about 0.6 mm. The copper disk was on the right of the interface—the zero coordinate.

Drawn from a figure by Correa da Silva and Mehl (3).

The copper-nickel alloys are not easy to make homogeneous. Other pairs of metals can be found in which the diffusive action is more rapid.

RELATIVE RATES OF DIFFUSION

A question that comes to mind concerns the rates at which two kinds of atoms move across an interface. In an assembly like the one in the previous section, is the number of nickel atoms entering the copper equal to the number of copper atoms entering the nickel? At first, metallurgists assumed that the rates were equal although some evidence had indicated the contrary. The question was answered in a convincing manner by an experiment in which the specimen shown in Fig. 7.3 was

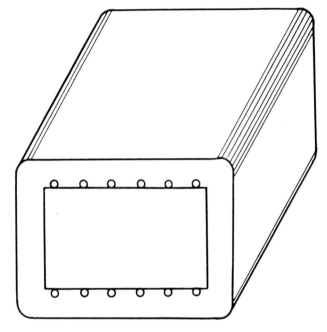

Fig. 7.3 Specimen for Determination of Relative Speeds of Diffusion of Copper and Zinc

The specimen consists of an alpha-brass bar on which copper has been electroplated. Molybdenum wires mark the interface between brass and copper. Heating the assembly to a temperature at which reasonably rapid diffusion took place caused the upper and lower rows of molybdenum marker wires to move toward each other. This action meant that the brass had decreased in volume and hence that it had lost more zinc atoms than it had gained copper atoms.

Redrawn from a figure by Smigelskas and Kirkendall (4).

used. The central part of this specimen was a bar of alpha brass containing approximately 30% zinc. On it was electroplated a heavy layer of unalloyed copper. At the junction between the bar and its coating fine molybdenum wires were inserted as a means of marking the original interface. Molybdenum does not alloy with either zinc or copper. After the specimen had been heated for 56 days at 785°C., the top and bottom rows of wires were nearly 0.01 in. closer together than they had been initially. The volume of the core had diminished by about 2.5%, apparently because the number of zinc atoms leaving exceeded the number of copper atoms entering and only a small part of the decrease could be accounted for by the smaller size of the copper atoms.

THE MECHANISM OF DIFFUSION

By what means atoms of one metal enter another metal and by what mechanism the alloy becomes more homogeneous in composition are matters that have been the subject of many technical papers. Also, a number of theories have been proposed.

The currently favored theory is based on the concept of "vacancies" or "lattice vacancies" concerning which more will be given in Chapter 15. With reference to the model of Fig. 3.8[2] a vacancy is the unoccupied space left if a ball is removed from the interior of the model. The equivalent removal of an atom from a metal is considered not to be followed by the squeezing down of the unoccupied space by surrounding atoms. What appears to happen is that one of the surrounding atoms, because of its thermal vibratory motion, moves into this space and thereby causes its original site to become a vacancy.

---

[2] A very large proportion of the investigations of diffusion in metals has been conducted on the face-centered cubic type. Hence, the frequent references made to Fig. 3.8.

In effect, the vacancy has moved. One might say that vacancies "diffuse."

Application of the theory of vacancies to the diffusion of atoms reveals that it can explain unequal rates of migration across a boundary between two joined metals. And microscopic evidence for the existence of vacancies can be found. It is obtained by an experiment not unlike that related to Fig. 7.3. In the brass piece, near its interface with the copper piece, may be seen tiny pores, or large vacancies, believed to have been caused by the coalescence of small vacancies created by the net outward movement of atoms.[3]

DIFFUSION OF A METAL'S OWN ATOMS (SELF-DIFFUSION)

A phenomenon that certainly does not contradict the idea of vacancies is the movement of atoms in a "pure," or unalloyed, metal. In this instance, the specimen is to be considered as homogeneous chemically and physically at all times. As all atoms of a metal behave identically, proof of such a movement might appear difficult. Actually, it is very simple. In recent years, several methods have been developed for converting one element into another. One method involves the use of a cyclotron. For example, if palladium is bombarded with protons in a cyclotron, it is converted into silver which, except for being radioactive, is chemically and physically the same as ordinary silver. In an experiment, radioactive silver was plated on a disk of ordinary silver. To this was welded another disk of ordinary silver. The result was a sandwich-type assembly consisting of a very thin layer of radioactive silver between two blocks of the ordinary kind as pictured in Fig. 7.4. After this assembly had been heated for nearly five days at about 875°C.,

---

[3] The reader will find Fig. 2 of Balluffi and Alexander (5) interesting in this connection.

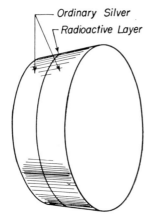

Ordinary Silver
Radioactive Layer

Fig. 7.4   Specimen for Study of Self-Diffusion

Radioactive silver, made by bombardment of palladium with protons in a cyclotron, is the filling in a sandwich of two thick disks of ordinary silver. Each disk is about $\frac{1}{4}$ in. thick. The radioactive silver layer is only 0.00015 in. thick.

Drawn from a description by Johnson (6).

the disks were tested for radioactivity at different distances from the joining plane. The extent to which the radioactive atoms diffused into the ordinary silver is shown in Fig. 7.5. Those that traveled farthest covered a distance of almost a millimeter.

DIFFUSION IN INTERSTITIAL SOLID SOLUTIONS

If the solid solution is composed of one element having atoms of ordinary size and one with exceptionally small atoms, diffusion seems to take place by a different mechanism. At least it takes place much more rapidly. The situation may be illustrated by the system iron and carbon.[4] An iron atom has a diameter of 2.56 Å whereas the diameter of a carbon atom is only 1.42 Å. When carbon goes into solution in iron, its atoms do not replace iron atoms, atom for atom, as when zinc goes into copper. Instead, they slip between the iron atoms, or, in metallurgical language, they occupy the "interstices"

---

[4] This description refers to iron in the face-centered cubic condition in which it exists above 910°C. The alloys of iron and carbon are covered in some detail in Chapter 9.

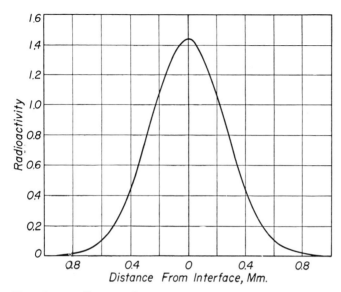

Fig. 7.5 Diffusion of Silver Through Itself

This graph shows the movement of radioactive silver atoms into the adjoining blocks of ordinary silver during a period of 4¾ days at 876°C. Maximum measurable penetration of the silver atoms was slightly less than 1 mm.
Johnson *(6).*

---

between the iron atoms. Obviously, unless some of the interstices are large enough to contain the carbon atoms with, perhaps, a tiny bit to spare, the iron atoms may have to move apart slightly. Figure 7.6 shows that the introduction of carbon does cause the iron atoms to move farther apart on the average.

DIFFUSION OF CARBON IN IRON

Apparently, small atoms like carbon can diffuse by moving from one interstitial position to another without

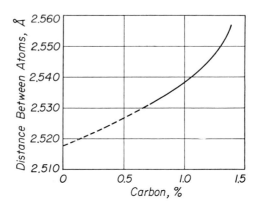

Fig. 7.6   Increase in Distance Between Iron Atoms as Carbon Is Added

This diagram is based on the high-temperature face-centered cubic form of iron, but the measurements were made at room temperature on quenched pieces and do not allow for expansion with temperature. This error is small, however.

This graph is redrawn from Öhman (7).

waiting for a vacancy. The relatively fast penetration of carbon into iron becomes evident upon comparison of Fig. 7.7 with Fig. 7.2. In the experiment from which the information for Fig. 7.7 was obtained, pieces of ordinary carbon steel were used. One had a carbon content of about 1.07% and the other, only 0.02%. They were welded end to end in a vacuum and then heated for about 61 hours at 925°C. The figure indicates that the carbon contents of both ends have been altered to a distance of about 5 millimeters from the interface.

The high mobility of carbon atoms at elevated temperature is an important factor in the heat treatment

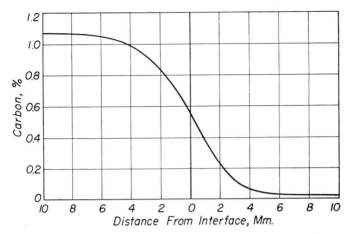

Fig. 7.7   Diffusion of Carbon in Steel

A steel containing 1.07% carbon was welded in a vacuum to a steel of only 0.02% carbon content. The welded specimen was then heated for 61.5 hr. at 925°C. with the result that carbon passed from the one steel to the other. Near the interface between the two pieces, indicated in the diagram by the vertical line at the center, the carbon content of the high-carbon piece decreased and that of the low-carbon piece increased. Note how much greater the distance of penetration is here than in Fig. 7.2.

This diagram was redrawn from Wells and Mehl (8).

---

of steel. It is of particular importance in carburizing operations. Rapid diffusion saves furnace time. As a practical matter, rate of penetration may be increased by raising the temperature of the carburizing treatment. However, the allowable temperature is limited by factors such as grain growth in and distortion of the piece and the allowable operating temperature of the furnace. The atoms of carbon for carburizing a piece must come

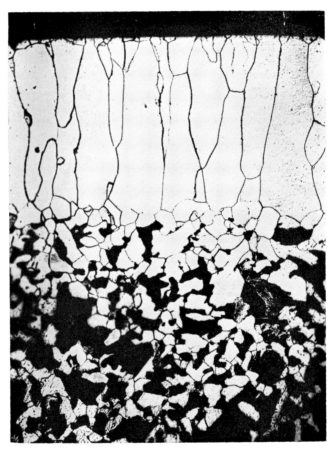

Fig. 7.8 Carbon Diffusion From Surface of Steel

The steel originally had a uniform carbon content and appeared at all points as in the lower portion. The carbon-containing portions etched black; hence, those portions of the specimen which have no black areas are devoid of carbon. This type of diffusion, known industrially as *decarburization*, is an important consideration in the heat treatment of steel. The specimen in this figure was decarburized in a laboratory experiment by being heated at 840°C. for 50 hr. in an atmosphere of hydrogen and water vapor.

Rowland and Upthegrove *(9).*   Magnification, 100×

from its surroundings. Introducing a carbonaceous gas around the steel is the most common way of providing the carbon atoms.

The high mobility of carbon atoms has its disadvantages also. Under some conditions, carbon may diffuse out of a piece of high-carbon steel and thereby convert the surface to a low-carbon product. Figure 7.8 shows an example of the loss of carbon by outward diffusion (decarburizing) and its effect on the microscopic appearance of the cross section near the surface of the piece. Obviously, if a uniform composition or a carbon-rich surface is needed, this loss of carbon can be unfortunate. Hydrogen, oxygen, and some other gases promote decarburizing action and, for this reason, the nature of the atmosphere in a heat-treating furnace is a matter of importance.

GASES CAN DIFFUSE THROUGH METALS

The mobility of small atoms indicated in the previous sections suggests that the atoms could migrate completely through a piece of metal if allowed sufficient time. Experience has shown that such migration is not unusual. For example, a pressure of hydrogen in excess of about 100,000 psi cannot be maintained in steel containers because the gas escapes through the walls even if they are an inch or two thick. Palladium permits only negligible amounts of hydrogen to diffuse through it at room temperature and a low pressure differential, but, at red heat, the hydrogen can pass through at an astonishing rate. Sheet palladium provided with a means for heating it can be used as a valve for admitting hydrogen to a closed space (system). An idea of the amount of hydrogen that can pass through nickel sheet at 248°C. is indicated in Fig. 7.9. With a vacuum on one side of a sheet of nickel 1 mm. (0.04 in.) thick and a pressure of about 1500 psi on the other, something

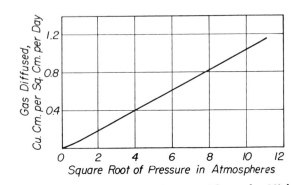

Fig. 7.9 Movement of Hydrogen Through Nickel— 248°C.

The nickel sheet was 1 mm. (0.04 in.) thick. The amount coming through the sheet is almost directly proportional to the square root of the difference in pressure on the two sides. In this experiment the pressure on one side was maintained at zero; that is, the space on one side of the sheet was evacuated. When the pressure of the hydrogen on the other side was 100 atmospheres, or, about 1500 psi., about 1 cu. cm. of hydrogen came through 1 sq. cm. of surface during 24 hr. This rate of flow is equivalent to 1/30 cu. ft. per sq. ft. of surface per day. This figure was taken from Smithells and Ransley *(10)*, but has been modified somewhat as to unit of flow.

---

like 1 cu. cm. of hydrogen will pass through 1 sq. cm. of surface per day. In English units, about 1/30 cu. ft. of hydrogen will pass through 1 sq. ft. in a day.

Other gases also can diffuse through metals. Oxygen moves through silver at 500°C. at a substantial rate. Nitrogen can pass through iron or molybdenum although the rate of flow is unimpressive.

CHEMICAL CHARACTER INFLUENCES RATE OF DIFFUSION

The chemical nature of gaseous atoms appears to have much to do with their capacity for going into solution in metals and for diffusing through them. Actually, solution and diffusion appear to be closely related. Nickel, through which hydrogen passes only slowly, can take only a small amount of this gas into solid solution. On the other hand, palladium, through which hydrogen diffuses readily, will absorb nearly a thousand times its own volume. Helium has relatively small atoms but it is inert chemically[5] and will neither dissolve in metals nor diffuse through them. Chemical character obviously is important to diffusion if one may judge from the behavior described above. However, it has been neglected here in comparison with the simpler mechanical aspects of the diffusion problem.

REFERENCES

1. W. C. Roberts-Austen: "On the Diffusion of Gold in Solid Lead at the Ordinary Temperature," *Proceedings, Royal Society*, London, Vol. 67, 1900, pp. 101–105.
2. F. Keller and R. H. Brown: "Diffusion in Alclad 24 S-T Sheet," *Transactions*, American Institute of Mining and Metallurgical Engineers, Vol. 156, 1944, pp. 377–386.
3. Luiz C. Correa da Silva and Robert F. Mehl: "Interface and Marker Movements in Diffusion in Solid Solutions of Metals," *Transactions*, American Institute of Mining and Metallurgical Engineers, Vol. 191, 1951, pp. 155–173.
4. A. D. Smigelskas and E. O. Kirkendall: "Zinc Diffusion in Alpha Brass," *Transactions*, American Institute of Mining and Metallurgical Engineers, Vol. 171, 1947, pp. 130–135.
5. R. Balluffi and B. H. Alexander: "Dimensional Changes Normal to Direction of Diffusion," *Journal of Applied Physics*, Vol. 23, 1952, pp. 953–956.
6. William A. Johnson: "The Self-Diffusion of Silver," *Transactions*, American Institute of Mining and Metallurgical Engineers, Vol. 143, 1941, pp. 107–111.

---

[5] Since this chapter was written, evidence has been presented that the inert gases of Column 18 of Fig. 1.1 are less inert than they were believed to be. In particular, xenon has been shown to be capable of forming compounds, apparently of an unstable nature.

7. Einar Öhman: "X-ray Investigations of the Crystal Structure of Hardened Steel," *Journal*, Iron and Steel Institute, Vol. 123, 1931, pp. 445–463.

8. Cyril Wells and Robert F. Mehl: "Rates of Diffusion of Carbon in Austenite in Plain Carbon, in Nickel and in Manganese Steels," *Transactions*, American Institute of Mining and Metallurgical Engineers, Vol. 140, 1940, pp. 279–306.

9. D. H. Rowland and Clair Upthegrove: "Grain Size and Its Influence on Surface Decarburization of Steel," *Transactions*, American Society for Metals, Vol. 24, 1936, pp. 96–125.

10. C. J. Smithells and C. E. Ransley: "Diffusion of Gases Through Metals, IV—The Diffusion of Oxygen and of Hydrogen Through Nickel at Very High Pressures," *Proceedings*, Royal Society, London, Vol. A157, 1936, pp. 292–302.

CHAPTER 8

Some Effects of Atomic Movements

THE EXAMPLES of migration of atoms described in the previous chapter were based on artificially established conditions. However, the information obtained from the experiments does lead to some understanding of the changes that take place in industrial alloys. It is, in fact, changes observed in the commercially useful alloys that have stimulated studies of the effects of atomic migration. This chapter will be devoted to some particularly useful and interesting effects of these atomic movements.

SIGNIFICANCE OF LINES *DF* AND *EG* IN THE LEAD-TIN DIAGRAM

When the lead-tin diagram of Fig. 5.2 was being considered, no explanation was given of the significance of the lines *DF* and *EG*. What these lines indicate are the limiting compositions for which the alloys can exist as solid solutions. As an illustration, *DF* indicates for an alloy containing less than 19.5% tin, how much of that tin will remain in solid solution at any temperature. For example, a 10% tin alloy will retain all of its tin in solid solution down to about 145°C., but at that temperature it begins to reject, or precipitate out, tin atoms. At 100°C., all tin in excess of 3.5% has been rejected. The extreme decrease in solubility in this alloy system is from 19.5% tin at 183°C., just as an alloy of this composition has completed solidification, to about 2% at 75°C. and below. The clue given by the diagram that the solubility of tin in lead decreases with temperature is the leftward deviation of *DF* as it descends to room temperature.

THE REJECTED TIN

Obviously, if the tin content of the solid solution is so reduced as the alloy cools, the tin atoms must go somewhere and one would think that some trace of them might be found. Actually, the tin atoms do assemble in little regions large enough to be seen under a microscope. It is these tiny aggregates[1] of tin that cause the mottled appearance of what would otherwise be uniformly dark gray lead-rich regions. As may be seen from Fig. 5.3 and Fig. 8.1, the mottling is observable in the primary crystals, that is, the regions that solidified above 183°C., and also in the lead-rich lamellar constituent of the eutectic region. It is particularly noticeable because of the light color of the tin as developed by the particular etchant used.

EFFECT OF RATE OF COOLING ON PRECIPITATION OF TIN

One is moved to ask what effect rate of cooling has on the amount of tin rejected from a lead-rich alloy. A

---

[1] Because of the curvature of the line *EG* in Fig. 5.2, one would suppose that some lead would be rejected from tin-rich regions as the temperature decreases. This action does go on; the tin particles contain lead in accordance with the compositions along *EG*. For example, tin particles rejected at 150°C. must contain about 1% lead. At 100°C., the proportion of lead would be extremely low as *EG* has practically disappeared into the right boundary (the 100% tin line).

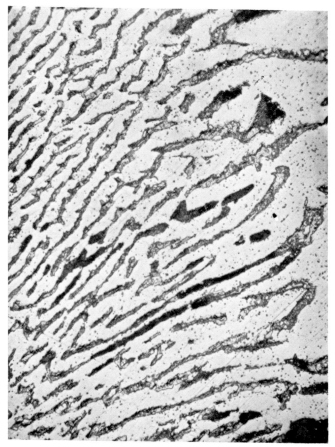

Fig. 8.1 Tin-Lead Alloy Containing 62% Tin

The laminated structure of the eutectic alloy pictured in Fig. 5.5 is here shown at a higher magnification. The dark laminae, mainly lead, are seen to be mottled by the tin coming out of solid solution. This action is the result of the decreasing solubility of tin in lead as the temperature falls.

Magnification, 500×

particular question is: Could a sufficiently drastic quenching prevent the tin atoms from coming out at all? The experimental evidence is that the tin atoms can be held in their high-temperature positions but that the situation is not permanent. Even if a quenched alloy containing 15% tin remains at room temperature, thin sheets of tin will form throughout the metal within two days' time. Further reduction of the temperature decreases the rate at which tin atoms come out of solid solution but the movement of tin continues at a detectable rate well below 0°C.

CHANGING SOLID SOLUBILITY—THE SOLVUS LINE

A decrease in solubility of one metal in another such as exists in the lead-tin system is relatively common among binary alloys. As indicated in a previous section, the clue to the existence of varying solid solubility in an alloy system is that the bounding line of the solid solution area curves, with descending temperature, in the manner of DF in the lead-tin diagram (Fig. 5.2). A line of this kind is called a "solvus" line, a name used frequently in descriptions of alloy systems. Often, a system exhibits decreasing solubility at both ends of the diagram. The lead-tin alloys do so but the solubility of lead in tin is small (2.5% maximum) compared with the solubility of tin in lead. Consequently, the effects are less evident and less interesting.

THE PRACTICAL USE OF CHANGES IN SOLUBILITY —AGE HARDENING

That the solid solubility of metal B in metal A changes with temperature is interesting scientifically. But if the fact had no industrial consequences, far less attention would have been paid to the phenomenon than has been. What is important is not that the atoms of B come out of A if the cooling is slow but that they can be trapped in their high-temperature positions if the cooling is fast, and that they can be allowed to come out under controlled conditions. The point is that by controlling the precipitation of atoms from a quenched alloy, the metallurgist can obtain a considerable increase in hardness and a corresponding increase in mechanical strength. Increase of hardness by this process is called "age hardening" or "precipitation hardening." How long a specimen must be held at what temperature in order that desired properties may be obtained depends upon the metals composing the alloy. In some instances, the hardening may take place at room temperature; in

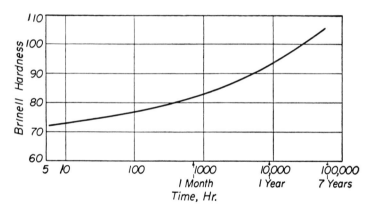

Fig. 8.2 Increase in Hardness of Aluminum Alloy With Time

This graph shows the effect of time on a quenched 5.6% copper, aluminum-copper alloy. The hardening is the result of the formation and precipitation of a substance that has very nearly the composition $CuAl_2$. This constituent is formed by the combination of copper atoms rejected by the solid solution with some of the aluminum atoms of that solution. The specimen remained at room temperature for seven years and was still increasing in hardness at the end of that time.
Redrawn from a figure presented by L. W. Kempf (1).

others, a temperature of several hundred degrees may be required if the increase is to occur within a practical time. An interesting example of increasing hardness in an alloy held at room temperature is presented in Fig. 8.2. The capacity of this aluminum-copper alloy to continue changing toward an equilibrium condition is interesting scientifically but probably few metallurgists would consider seven years a practical heat treating time. If tungsten atoms are trapped in iron by a quenching operation, the quenched piece would not be likely to show a noticeable change in hardness if held at room temperature for many years. Even if it were held at 500°C., hardness would increase only at a slow rate. However, at 700°C. the increase in hardness is relatively rapid as indicated in Fig. 8.3.

A change of property that may be as important as those of hardness and strength is the decrease in ductil-

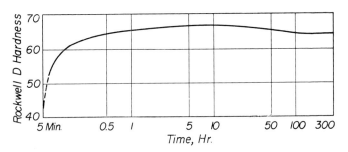

Fig. 8.3   Increase in Hardness of Iron-Tungsten Alloy

The alloy contained about 24% tungsten. It was quenched from a high temperature and then reheated at 700°C. for the times indicated along the base of the graph. The alloy passed through its maximum hardness after about 20 hr. at this temperature. Iron-tungsten alloys do not age perceptibly at room temperature and very slowly even at 500°C., but at 700°C., they reach a comparatively high hardness in a few minutes.

This graph was redrawn from Sykes (2).

ity. In some instances, the reduction in ductility can be tolerated; in others, it destroys the usefulness of the alloy. Aluminum alloys usually belong in the first category. They show some decrease in ductility upon aging but not to a degree to impair their usefulness. On the other hand, the remarkable increase in hardness that aging produces in iron-molybdenum alloys is associated with an equally remarkable loss of ductility. Hence, these alloys are unimportant industrially.

AN AGE-HARDENING ALUMINUM ALLOY

When age hardening was observed in an aluminum alloy in 1912, no one was able to understand why such a change should take place. In fact, the problem was not solved until several years afterward. At the present time if a metallurgist has access to a constitutional diagram for a pair of metals, he can tell at a glance whether age-hardening effects are likely to occur. For example, the line DF in Fig. 8.4 has a characteristic curving trend that suggests that aluminum-copper alloys should show age-hardening effects. Figure 8.4 is useful in a study of these alloys but if numerical values are needed, a larger scale diagram of the important area is convenient. Such a diagram is given in Fig. 8.5. From it, one sees that the κ (kappa) solid solution may contain as much as 5.6% copper at a temperature slightly below 550°C. but that at 200°C., it can contain only 0.5% or less than 1/10 as much.

From the industrially important age-hardening aluminum alloys, the 4% copper alloy may be selected for illustration of the precipitation-hardening process. Also, for simplicity, the simple binary alloy will be considered. Aluminum can hold 4% copper in solid solution over the range from 490°C. to 585°C. If such an alloy is cooled slowly, it begins to reject copper atoms at 490°C. (point b) and does so rapidly down to about 300°C. below which temperature the rate of rejection is much less as indicated by the nearly vertical trend of DF.

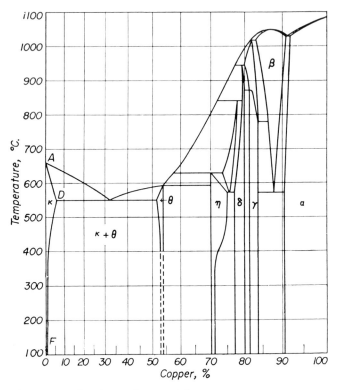

Fig. 8.4 Aluminum-Copper Diagram

An alloy, having a composition corresponding to any of the six composition ranges denoted by Greek letters, appears under the microscope as a simple, homogeneous substance. An alloy in any of the five fields between the lettered regions has two microscopic constituents—the lettered constituents at either end of the field. (Note that the horizontal scale is inverse logarithmic, to open up the diagram at the right end, where lines are most numerous.)

SOME EFFECTS OF ATOMIC MOVEMENTS   119

Fig. 8.5   Aluminum Side of Aluminum-Copper Diagram

This figure shows the decrease of the solubility of copper in
aluminum as the temperature decreases. An alloy cooled slowly from a temperature above *DF* (but below *AD*) begins to
reject copper from solid solution as its temperature reaches
the line *DF*. For example, the alloy containing 4% copper
begins to reject that element at the point *b*. When the alloy
has cooled to 200°C., it will have only 0.5% copper left in
solution.

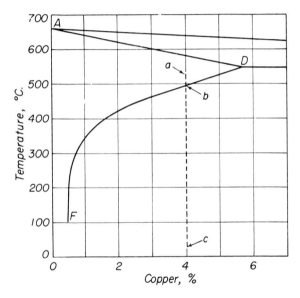

When the alloy reaches temperature *c*, it has lost, or rejected,[2] about ⅞ of the copper it contained at points *a*
and *b*, that is, above 490°C. On the other hand, if such
an alloy is cooled very rapidly from *a* to *c*, as by quench-

---

[2] To say that copper has been rejected from the solid solution does
not mean that it has been thrust physically outside the entire mass
of alloy. Rejection as used here means much the same that it did
in the description of the lead-tin alloys.

ing, its copper atoms will not have time to move out of their high temperature positions. That they will not remain in place indefinitely was shown in Fig. 8.2.

Figure 8.4 does not merely indicate that the solid solubility of copper in aluminum changes with temperature. It specifies, also, the composition of the rejected substance which, in this instance, is a compound designated as θ that has nearly but not exactly the proportions corresponding to $CuAl_2$. The reason that one knows that θ is the substance rejected by solid solution κ is that θ is the homogeneous substance[3] nearest to κ on the diagram.

THE EFFECT OF TEMPERATURE ON THE HARDENING BEHAVIOR

Practical use of the age-hardening effect in the aluminum-copper alloys requires that the temperature be raised so that the increased hardness and strength may be attained in a relatively short time. How the temperature at which a 4% copper alloy is aged affects the rate at which it hardens and its maximum hardness is apparent from Fig. 8.6. If maintained at 110°C., the alloy attains maximum hardness in about 230 days after which it begins to soften. If the temperature is increased to 240°C., maximum hardness is reached in 1/20 day or a little over one hour. However, the maximum hardness

---

[3] A diagram like Fig. 8.4 tells the reader that as the proportion of a second component, copper in this instance, is increased, a series of homogeneous substances is brought into being and exists for an interval of composition. In Fig. 8.4, the substances existing over composition intervals at room temperature are marked α, γ, δ, η, θ, and κ. Compound θ exists from about 53.5% to 54% Cu. The next homogeneous substance bears the designation η. It exists from about 75% to 76% Cu. Alloys having compositions that do not correspond to a homogeneous substance are composed of mixtures of two of these substances. For example, an alloy containing 30% Cu is made up of about equal parts of κ and θ as a microscopic examination would make evident. Figure 8.4 has been drawn in a reversed position from that customarily used. Hence, the alphabetical designations run in a reverse order.

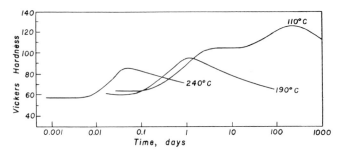

Fig. 8.6   The Effect of Aging Temperature on Rate of Increase of Hardness and on Maximum Hardness

As aging temperature increases from 110°C. to 240°C., the length of time to reach maximum hardness decreases from 230 days to about 1 hour. Also evident from the graph is the lower hardness obtained at the higher temperature.
Drawn from graphs by Hardy (3, 4).

---

attained at the higher temperature is considerably less. A feature of the 110°C. curve that is not present in the other two is the two intervals of rising hardness separated by a plateau. The reason for the plateau is explained, in part, in the following section.

THE MECHANISM OF AGE HARDENING

A detailed study of age hardening in aluminum-copper alloys shows that the process is not a simple matter of forming particles of θ compound. Instead four distinct kinds of particles may be formed under different conditions, particularly at different temperatures. The first two are neither compounds nor solid solutions in the ordinary sense and are called "zones." The other two are compounds, one of which is still tied to the parent solid solution, κ phase, in a special way.

The first type of particle actually is a little group of copper atoms that have come out of the κ solid solution and assembled themselves into the shape of a disk. These disks are not more than one or two layers of atoms thick and usually are less than a millionth of a centimeter in diameter. The disks are shown in Fig 8.7 in which they are seen edgewise at a magnification of 1,000,000 diam-

Fig. 8.7 Plate-Shaped Assemblies of Precipitated Atoms Formed in Initial Stage of Hardening

This transmission electron micrograph shows that the first particles formed by precipitation appear as needles when seen in cross section. Actually, the particles are tiny disk-shaped assemblies of, mainly, copper atoms. The assemblies are called G.P.[1] zones. Extraneous effects from the passage of electrons through the metal introduce dark areas and other confusing markings so that the needles do not stand out clearly. Courtesy, J. B. Nicholson and J. Nutting, Department of Metallurgy, University of Cambridge.

Magnification, 1,000,000×

eters. Unfortunately, extra effects resulting from the passage of electrons through the specimen produce dark areas and generally "spoil the view." These particles are called G.P.[1][4] zones. They are responsible for the initial rise in hardness in the 110°C. curve of Fig. 8.6.

The second type of particle is called a G.P.[2] zone. A typical unit of G.P.[2] structure may be imagined to consist of five layers of which the central one is composed entirely of copper atoms, the two outer layers are made up entirely of aluminum atoms, and the other two layers contain both kinds. The relative number of copper and aluminum atoms on the intermediate layers is such as to bring the composition of the entire assembly near to the proportion in $CuAl_2$. Like the G.P.[1] zones, the disks of G.P.[2] material gather on (100) type planes of the parent solid solution. They cause the second rise in hardness on the 110°C. curve.

Particles of the third type are called θ' because their structure has some resemblance to that of θ particles. They are shaped like tiny plates and form on (100) type planes. Their atoms have definite positions; hence they are true compounds. They are not independent, however, as the spacing of their atoms is controlled to a considerable degree by the parent solid solution. In other words, they are "coherent" with the κ material. The strain that is developed in the κ substance because of its effort to control the positions of the atoms in θ' appears to be responsible for the hardness and strength of the alloy as a whole.

The fourth product is θ compound. It may be formed by the allotropic transformation (see Chapter 11) from θ' or by direct rejection from solid solution. The positions of its atoms are not controlled by the κ phase; hence, its presence does little to increase hardness. In

[4] The G and P stand for Guinier and Preston, two men who individually discovered the nature of these zones.

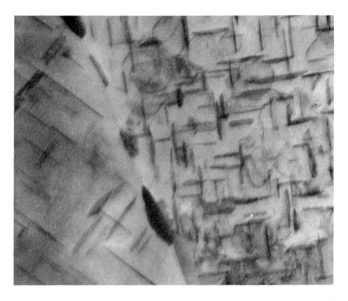

Fig. 8.8   Particles of Θ and Θ′ Substance in an Aged Aluminum-Copper Alloy

The particles of θ' are relatively large compared with the G.P.[1] zones of the previous figure and they are true compounds. They are disk- or plate-shaped and lie parallel to planes of (100) type. The blobs in the grain boundary are θ substance. A few of the particles within the grains appear to be in the process of changing from the θ' to the θ condition. The atomic arrangement in θ particles is not related to the structure of the surrounding solid solution. In this respect, the θ particles differ from the θ' particles. θ particles form in the late stages of aging and at relatively high temperatures. If they are present in large numbers, the alloy is likely to have passed its peak of hardness.

Courtesy, J. B. Nicholson and J. Nutting, Department of Metallurgy, University of Cambridge. Magnification, 22,000×

Fig. 8.8, the θ material appears as blobs, mainly in grain boundaries, whereas the θ' particles appear as needle-shaped in cross section and are oriented with respect to the κ substance.

A THIRD ELEMENT INFLUENCES AGE HARDENING

Addition of a third element has a profound effect on the hardening action in a binary alloy. Figure 8.9 and Fig. 8.10 show, respectively, the effect of magnesium and of iron on the aging process in aluminum-copper alloys. Magnesium produces a marked decrease in the time to reach maximum hardness at 190°C. and causes some increase in hardness. Iron slows up the aging process as

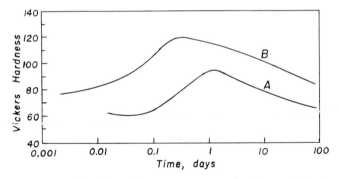

Fig. 8.9   The Effect of Magnesium on the Rate of Hardening and on the Maximum Hardness of an Aluminum-Copper Alloy Containing 4% Copper

The addition of 0.57% magnesium produced a marked reduction in the time to reach maximum hardness and a considerable increase in maximum hardness. The aging temperature was 190°C. for both curves. Curve A shows the effect with no magnesium; curve B shows the effect with magnesium added.
Hardy (3, 5).

indicated in Fig. 8.10. At low temperature, it may stop the aging action altogether in an alloy that otherwise would show this effect.

Aging processes in complex alloys are complicated and not easy to understand in detail. The 4% copper alloy known as Duralumin contains, also, magnesium, silicon

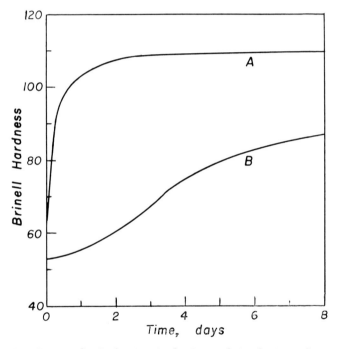

Fig. 8.10   The Reduction in the Rate of Hardening of an Aluminum-Copper Alloy by the Addition of Iron

The presence of about 0.6% iron reduces the rate of hardening in a striking manner. The specimens contained about 4% copper. They were heated at 150°C. Curve *A* shows the rate with no iron; curve *B* shows the rate with iron added. Gayler (*6*).

and, usually, iron. At room temperature it reaches maximum hardness in a few days' time. In fact, rivets of this material often are kept in dry ice (solid CO_2) to prevent hardening before use.

GENERAL COMMENTS ON AGE HARDENING

Although the aluminum-copper alloy served for illustration of age hardening, it is only one of a group of commercially important age-hardenable alloys not only of aluminum but of other metals. Copper to which a per cent or two of beryllium has been added can be quenched and aged to produce tools and other objects of good hardness and strength. If a bit of cobalt is added to the alloy, still better results are obtained. Age hardening is used to increase the hardness of some special types of steel. It also makes possible superior properties in some permanent magnet alloys. Some nickel-base alloys intended for parts to be operated at high temperature are of age-hardening type.

REFERENCES

1. L. W. Kempf: Discussion on pp. 113–116 of "Effect of Quenching Strains on Lattice Parameter and Hardness Values of High Purity Aluminum-Copper Alloys," by Arthur Phillips and R. M. Brick, *Transactions,* American Institute of Mining and Metallurgical Engineers, Vol. 111, 1934, pp. 94–112.

2. "Age-Hardening of Metals," Symposium, American Society for Metals, 1940, 448 pages. See article by W. P. Sykes, pp. 82–116.

3. H. K. Hardy: "The Ageing Characteristics of Binary Aluminium-Copper Alloys," *Journal,* Institute of Metals, Vol. 79, 1951, pp. 321–369.

4. H. K. Hardy: "Ageing Curves at 110° C. on Binary and Ternary Aluminium-Copper Alloys," *Journal,* Institute of Metals, Vol. 82, 1953–54, pp. 236–238.

5. H. K. Hardy: "The Ageing Characteristics of Some Ternary Aluminium-Copper-Magnesium Alloys With Cop-

per: Magnesium Weight Ratios of 7:1 and 2.2:1," *Journal,* Institute of Metals, Vol. 83, 1954–55, pp. 17–34.

6. Marie L. V. Gayler: "The Effect of the Addition of Small Percentages of Iron and Silicon to a High-Purity 4 Per-Cent. Copper-Aluminium Alloy," *Journal,* Institute of Metals, Vol. 60, 1937, pp. 75–98.

CHAPTER 9

Iron, Steel, and the A₃ Transformation

ANTHROPOLOGISTS OFTEN CLASSIFY types of civilizations according to the material used for tools and utensils. They speak of the *stone age*, the *age of bronze* and so on. According to this scheme, the present period may well be called the *age of steel* and the date of its beginning set at 1855. Although steel has been known and used for thousands of years, its production on the present scale was not possible before the development of modern processes of which the first was devised by Bessemer in the year mentioned. The low cost of production by these methods and the consequent greatly increased use of steel constitute a basic contribution to the present industrial era. If a civilization is to be named for its toolmaking materials, then surely we are living in an age of steel.

IRON CHANGES THE ARRANGEMENT OF ITS ATOMS

From the viewpoint of this book, the interesting aspect of the whole matter is that the production of steel tools and the industrial civilization which is so largely the result of that production depend upon a property of iron which of itself seems to be of little importance. This property is the ability to change from one atomic arrangement to another. At room temperature, iron has the body-centered cubic arrangement illustrated in Fig. 3.5, but if it is heated, it changes at 910°C. to the face-centered cubic structure depicted in Fig. 3.8. For convenience, we may refer hereafter to the low-temperature form as *alpha iron* and to the high-temperature form as *gamma iron*[1] in accordance with the general system (Chapter 8). If heated to still higher temperatures it changes back at 1390°C. to the body-centered cubic arrangement, here called *delta* iron.

THE A_3 TRANSFORMATION

Metallurgists call a change in the atomic arrangement of a metal a *transformation* and give the specific name A_3 *transformation* to the one which occurs in iron at 910°C. The A_3 transformation is complicated by the peculiarity that it occurs at 910°C. when the temperature is rising, and at about 900°C. when the temperature is falling—an unexplained lag or hysteresis. This situation is a trifle annoying when one wishes to indicate the transformation on a constitutional diagram. It is also conducive to a certain inexactness; for although 910°C. frequently is taken as the true temperature of the change, the less exact term, 900°C. transformation, also is employed. Because of this difference in temperature, the change on heating is called Ac_3 and on cooling Ar_3.

---

[1] When face-centered cubic iron takes other elements into solid solution, as when alloyed with carbon, it is called *austenite*—a microscopist's term—or *gamma phase*. Similarly, if body-centered iron takes one or more other elements into solution, it may be called *ferrite* or *alpha phase*. (As alpha iron will not take much carbon into solution, the alpha phase field is very narrow in the iron-carbon system as may be seen from Fig. 9.7.)

CHANGE IN DIMENSIONS

The A₃ transformation reveals itself in various ways. One of the most commonly observed is by change in dimensions. If a bar of iron is heated above room temperature, its length increases very nearly in proportion to the rise in temperature. However, instead of increasing steadily in length up to the melting point, the bar short-

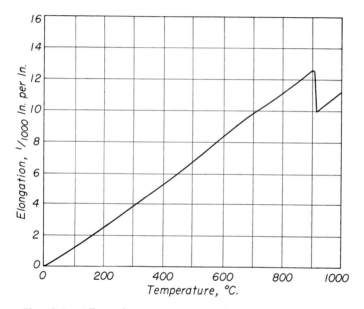

Fig. 9.1   Effect of Temperature on Iron Rod

The rod lengthens at a comparatively steady rate until it reaches the transformation temperature, about 910°C. Then it shortens abruptly by about 20% of its previous extension. This shortening occurs because the atoms suddenly assume a more compact arrangement; that is, one in which they are more closely packed together.

This curve has been redrawn from Walters and Gensamer (1).

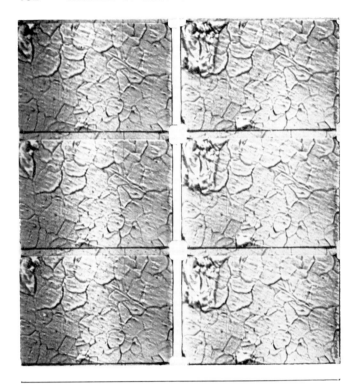

ens suddenly upon reaching the A_3 temperature (Fig. 9.1) and then continues to lengthen.

A more striking effect is observed if one watches a polished specimen of iron through a microscope. The action is illustrated in Fig. 9.2 which shows parts of a motion picture depicting the progress of transformation in a sample of coarse-grained, unalloyed iron. In the first vertical strip, most of the area shows only the grain boundaries that developed on the surface at about 700°C. as the specimen was being heated, but in the upper left-hand corner the transformation is beginning.

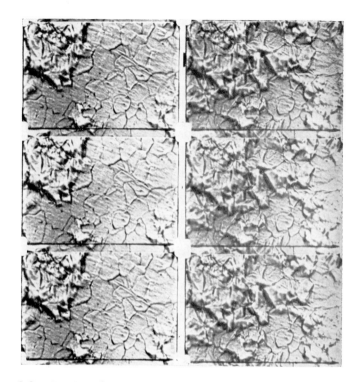

Fig. 9.2 A₃ Transformation of Coarse-Grained Iron

In the first vertical strip (opposite page), most of the area displays only the grain boundaries that developed on the surface at about 700°C. as the specimen was being heated, but in the upper left hand corner, the transformation is beginning. The second strip shows considerable extension of the area in the corner, a new area near the bottom and slightly left of center and, faintly, a third region at the lower right. In the third strip (above), all of these areas have increased in size, and in the fourth strip, the transformation is becoming general.

The second strip shows considerable extension of the area in the corner, a new area near the bottom and slightly left of center, and faintly, a third region at the lower right. In the third strip, all of these areas have increased in size, and in the fourth, the transformation is general.

THE HEAT EFFECT

Another effect of transformation of which much use has been made in investigations of iron and steel is the absorption of heat as iron is heated through the Ac_3 change and the corresponding evolution of heat when it cools through the Ar_3 temperature. These effects are similar to the absorption of heat when a metal melts and the release of heat when it solidifies, also, to the comparable effects when ice melts and water freezes. In a transformation, the atoms of the substance change from one fixed configuration to another fixed configuration. In melting or freezing, they change from a fixed arrangement to a mobile, liquid condition, or vice-versa. In each kind of event, the temperature of the substance remains unchanged while the action is going on.

The interval of time during which a specimen of transforming iron remains at constant temperature permits a simple demonstration of the phenomenon. One notes the length of time required by the specimen to rise through a definite temperature interval such as 1°C. or 2°C. and plots these time intervals against the temperature as in Fig. 9.3. The very long period for a rise of 1°C. at 910°C. is evident. This graph is plotted with the temperature along the horizontal axis in accordance with the general engineering practice of plotting the independent variable horizontally. In most instances, especially if the curve is plotted automatically, the temperature appears along the vertical axis.

CHANGE IN MAGNETIC PROPERTIES

The change in magnetic character during the A_3 transformation is fully as striking as the alteration in length

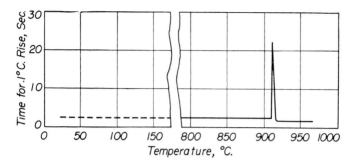

Fig. 9.3   Slowing of Temperature Rise at A₃ Point

For any temperature, the distance of the graph above the base line indicates the number of seconds spent in rising 1°C. When the transformation sets in, the metal continues to absorb heat with practically no change in temperature. Hence, instead of increasing 1°C. in temperature every 2 or 3 sec. as it has been doing, the specimen occupies a considerable part of a minute in rising the next 1°. In this experiment, the temperature of the furnace rose at a constant rate. This graph is based on data from Merica (2).

and the heat effect. Also, it can be made to furnish information concerning the rate of conversion from one crystalline form to the other at different stages of transformation. Iron is not ferromagnetic at the transformation temperature because, as it is heated, it loses this characteristic at about 770°C. and becomes paramagnetic.[2] The degree to which a metal is paramagnetic

[2] A ferromagnetic substance has a magnetic effect disproportionately strong in comparison with the magnetic field that is magnetizing it. As commonly stated, the ratio of the flux density to the magnetizing field—the permeability—is large. Also, it varies with the strength of the magnetizing field. In a paramagnetic substance, the ratio is smaller and is constant regardless of field strength. In fact, the permeability is near one for all paramagnetic metals. Usually, the magnetic character of a paramagnetic substance is not indicated in terms of permeability but in a different unit called the susceptibility. This unit indicates minor changes in the paramagnetism of a substance more distinctly.

commonly is stated as its susceptibility. During the A_3 transformation in unalloyed iron, the magnetic susceptibility shifts suddenly by a factor of about 8. If the iron is especially free from contaminating elements, a graph of the changes in susceptibility with temperature has the nearly rectangular form shown in Fig. 9.4. The two sides of the rectangle correspond to the changes in susceptibility at the Ar_3 and Ac_3 points. A few thousandths of a per cent of some impurity may deform the loop drastically.

A study of the change in susceptibility during successive time intervals, as the transformation progresses, reveals that the conversion is most rapid near midpoint. Also of interest is the interval of about 8°C. between Ar_3, the left side of the loop, and Ac_3, the right side. Although physical chemists and theorists in general have believed that the temperature of both changes should be the same, some doubt exists whether even purer iron and lower rates of transformation can reduce this difference.

OTHER CHANGES

Other changes do take place during the A_3 transformation but they are less spectacular than the three that have been described. The change in electrical resistance, for example, is almost undetectable.

WHAT CARBON DOES

The addition of even small percentages of carbon changes the properties of iron in many ways. For one thing, it depresses the temperature of the beginning of transformation in a cooling specimen from 900°C., the Ar_3 point, to about 720°C. for an alloy containing 0.80% carbon. Although the curve in Fig. 9.5 suggests that still higher percentages of carbon would depress the transformation still more, no test can be made of this point because of the interference to be described in the next section.

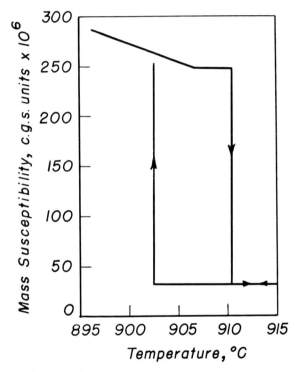

Fig. 9.4   The Change in Magnetic Susceptibility With Temperature During the A₃ Transformation in Iron

This specimen was exceptionally free from contaminating substances. During the experiment, it was held in an evacuated silica container. The complete cycle of heating and cooling lasted 10 hours or more.

Rogers and Stamm (3).

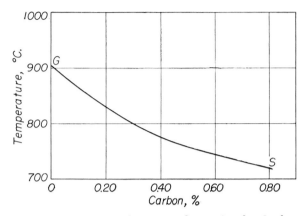

Fig. 9.5   Depression of A₃ Transformation by Carbon

This graph shows the temperature of the beginning of transformation in slowly cooled iron-carbon alloys (steel) containing up to about 0.80% carbon. For all but very low carbon contents, the change is not completed until the temperature has fallen to about 720°C. (See Fig. 9.7).

Chapter 8 contained several illustrations of alloys in which the solubility of one element in another decreases with falling temperature. For example, the solubility of copper in aluminum was shown to decrease from about 5.6% at 548°C. to about 0.5% at 200°C. The same type of thing happens in the iron-carbon alloys. The solubility of carbon in iron decreases from about 1.7% at 1135° C. to approximately 0.80% at 720°C. If it were not for the transformations that occur in iron, the iron-carbon diagram very probably would appear as in Fig. 9.6. In this diagram, the solvus, or solubility line, *ES*, is real and well established down to the temperature *S* (720°C.) but below this point it is fictitious.

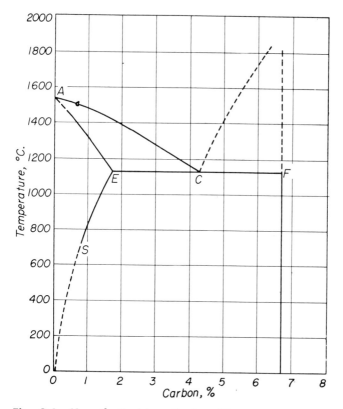

Fig. 9.6 Hypothetical Iron-Carbon Diagram

If iron had no transformation points, the iron-carbon diagram probably would appear as shown above. The line *ES* and its dotted extension show how the solubility of carbon in iron decreases with temperature. For example, an alloy containing 1% carbon begins to precipitate carbon at 820°C. when cooling slowly from a higher temperature. According to the diagram, it would reject nearly all of its carbon before reaching room temperature.

THE IRON-CARBON DIAGRAM

The complete diagram incorporating the line *GS* from Fig. 9.5 and the line *ES* from Fig. 9.6 is exhibited in Fig. 9.7. All of the lines in this diagram are real and well established lines; but, as a means of emphasizing the importance of the transformation, the only lines drawn full

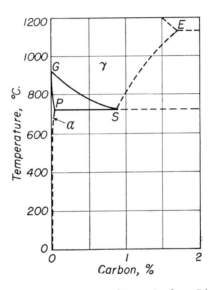

Fig. 9.7 Important Part of Iron-Carbon Diagram

This figure shows the part of the iron-carbon diagram that is important for the heat treatment of steel. The reader will note how the line *GS* from Fig. 9.5 fits into this diagram as *GS*. Line *ES* was seen previously in Fig. 9.6. Line *PS* indicates the ending of the transformation for all alloys except those containing very little carbon. The very low carbon alloys are completely transformed before they reach the temperature of *PS*, 720°C.

are *GS* which marks its beginning[3] and the branched line *GPS* which marks its end. The temperature of the horizontal line *PS*, corresponding to the end of transformation of alloys from 0.03 to 0.80% carbon, is called the A_1 point because of the pronounced heat evolution observed when a cooling alloy reaches this temperature.

As long as the temperature of an alloy—or steel, as the industrial product is called—remains above the line *GSE* the presence of the carbon has little effect on the arrangement of the iron atoms except to increase their average interatomic distance slightly as shown in Fig. 7.6. However, carbon does complicate the transformation experienced by the cooling alloy. The nature of the complication depends much on the rate of cooling. In fact, rate of cooling is so important that the remainder of this chapter will be devoted to a description of the transformation in slowly cooled steels and the entire next chapter will be concerned with the transformation in rapidly cooled steels.

COOLING THROUGH THE TRANSFORMATION RANGE

The effect of slow passage through the Ar_3 transformation—often called cooling through the Ar_3-Ar_1 range or through the critical range—may be illustrated by an examination of some representative steels. The first is a steel containing about 0.25% carbon. A steel of this composition cools from a temperature of 1000°C. or 1200°C. quite uneventfully until it reaches a temperature of about 825°C. where it touches the line *GS*. At this point, the tendency for the iron to transform to the low-temperature, body-centered cubic form can no longer be restrained by 0.25% carbon and some of the iron atoms begin taking up the low-temperature arrangement.

---

[3] This description refers to a cooling alloy. With rising temperature, *GS* would correspond to the end of the transformation.

The alpha iron formed as the result of this transformation does not have the capacity for taking carbon into solid solution that gamma iron does. Consequently, the carbon atoms move from the transforming regions into the regions that have not transformed, that is, into the remaining face-centered cubic gamma, or austenitic, portion. The proportion of alloy that has transformed, if cooling is slow, depends only on the temperature. At 760°C., the relative amounts of transformed and untransformed alloy are about as shown in Fig. 9.8. This picture represents the alloy as it exists after being quenched from 760°C. The light areas are the transformed material and the dark areas represent the untransformed. The part that had already transformed was changed very little as the result of quenching whereas the part that had not transformed at high temperature underwent the typical transforming action that takes place in a steel of the same (now perhaps 0.50%) carbon content. If the piece is held at a constant temperature after it has been partially converted to the alpha form—for example, if the specimen of Fig. 9.8 remains at 760°C.—no more action takes place. However, if it is allowed to cool, more of it is transformed into the alpha form, that is, into ferrite. Correspondingly, the region of untransformed alloy decreases in volume but becomes richer in carbon. Simultaneously, this portion undergoes a lowering of its transformation temperature. The action here has a strong similarity to the freezing of the lead-tin alloys. As cooling continues, the composition and temperature of the untransformed portion follow a succession of points along *GS* (Fig. 9.7); at the same time the composition and temperature of the transformed portion (ferrite) follow along *GP*.

HOW THE TRANSFORMATION ENDS

The movement of carbon from the portions transforming into ferrite continues until the unconverted portion,

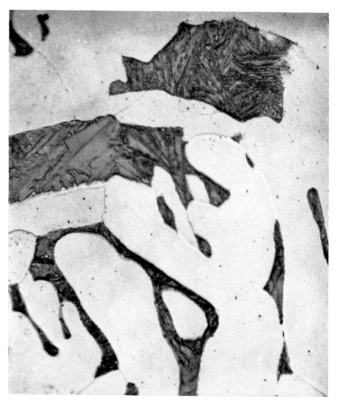

Fig. 9.8 Partially Transformed Low-Carbon Steel

This specimen of 0.25% carbon steel was quenched while in the process of transforming. The light-colored portions had been converted to the low-temperature form but the dark areas were still unchanged when the specimen was quenched. Carbon had moved out of the light-colored regions into the dark ones so that the composition of the alloy was no longer uniform.

Courtesy, Division of Metallurgy, National Bureau of Standards.   Magnification, 1500×

Fig. 9.9 Slowly Cooled Steel—0.25% Carbon

The light-colored areas represent iron in the low-temperature form. They contain very little carbon. Also, they are identical with the light-colored areas of the previous figure. The laminated structure was formed at 720°C. from the relatively high-carbon, untransformed regions that appear dark in Fig. 9.8. The alternate layers of this laminated structure are iron (light) and iron carbide (dark).

Courtesy, F. F. Lucas, Bell Telephone Laboratories, Inc.

Magnification, 2500×

[144]

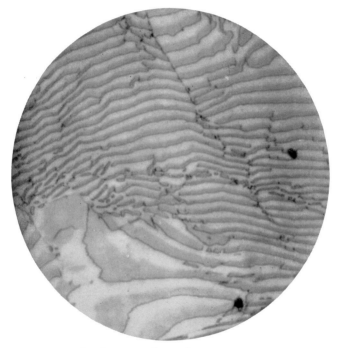

Fig. 9.10 Slowly Cooled Steel—0.80% Carbon

Steel of this composition transforms entirely at a single temperature, about 720°C., into alternate plates of iron (light) and iron carbide (dark). As in most examples of this structure, these laminae are curved and irregular. Along the rim at the top left, the plates appear to be almost exactly perpendicular to the plane of the polished surface, whereas at the lower left, they are nearly parallel to it. This picture gives an unusually good idea of the relative proportion of iron and iron carbide. Lucas (*4*).   Magnification, 2500×

the austenite, attains the carbon content corresponding to point S, which it does at 720°C. If the remaining austenite were to take up a little more carbon, it would be in a supersaturated condition in which its normal behavior is to reject the amount of carbon that is in excess of the limit of solubility—0.80% carbon at 720°C. An impasse has been reached in which no further transformation can take place because the remaining austenite will not accept any more carbon. The solution of this problem is that the austenite transforms into ferrite and simultaneously rejects carbon. The carbon behaves similarly to the copper rejected from aluminum in one respect; it forms a compound with the metal from which it is precipitated. In this instance, the compound has the formula Fe_3C. It is called "iron carbide" by chemists and "cementite" by microscopists. The metallographic result of the simultaneous conversion to ferrite and formation of iron carbide from rejected carbon is that the austenite remaining at 720°C. is converted to an assembly of alternate layers of iron and iron carbide as depicted in Fig. 9.9. Naturally, the portions that have already transformed, the light areas in the figure, are not affected.

THE TRANSFORMATION IN HIGHER CARBON STEELS

Carbon steel of 0.80%C demonstrates no tendency to change until it cools to 720°C., whereupon it undergoes both transformation and formation of iron carbide simultaneously. The result, as observed microscopically, is that the whole specimen is converted at the single temperature S to a laminated structure of iron and iron carbide resembling Fig. 9.10. This structure, called *pearlite*, is of the same character as the laminated area of the previous figure. In both figures, the lighter constituent of the pearlitic structure is iron and the darker is iron carbide.

The pearlitic structure in Fig. 9.10 has an obvious resemblance to the 62% tin alloy shown in Fig. 5.5. Because of this resemblance and even more because of the similarity of the configuration of lines in Figs. 9.7 and

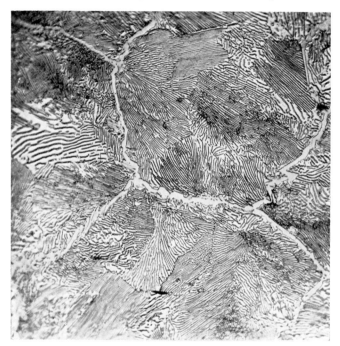

Fig. 9.11   Slowly Cooled Steel—1.25% Carbon

When steels with a carbon content above 0.80% are cooled slowly, iron carbide is deposited in the grain boundaries as shown in this figure. The decreasing solubility of carbon in iron is the cause of the precipitation. At 720°C., the grains themselves are converted into the laminated structures seen here. At a higher magnification this pearlitic structure would be similar to that in the previous figure.

Courtesy, Division of Metallurgy, National Bureau of Standards.   Magnification, 500×

5.2, the structure in Fig. 9.10 is called a "eutectoid structure." More is given on the subject in Chapter 11.

Steel containing 1.25% carbon can cool undisturbedly only to about 900°C. At this temperature, it encounters the solubility line *ES* and begins to precipitate iron carbide. As the specimen continues to cool, it rejects more carbide. This carbide is not distributed in small particles throughout the grains, as was the copper compound precipitated from the reheated aluminum alloy described in the previous chapter, but gathers in the grain boundaries.[4] This behavior is apparent in Fig. 9.11 which shows the grain boundaries delineated by carbide that was precipitated as the steel cooled from 900 to 720°C. At 720°C., as a consequence of their rejection of carbon, the grains proper had been reduced to 0.80% carbon; hence, they decomposed into iron and iron carbide in the manner described for the two previous specimens. The laminae appear thinner in this pearlite mainly because of the lower magnification, but the rate of cooling may have been a little more rapid in this specimen, and the rate of cooling does influence the thickness of laminae.

REFERENCES

1. Francis M. Walters, Jr. and M. Gensamer: "A Dilatometric Study of Iron-Manganese Binary Alloys," *Transactions,* American Society for Steel Treating, Vol. 19, 1931–1932, pp. 608–621.

2. P. D. Merica: "A Simplification of the Inverse Rate Method for Thermal Analysis," *Bureau of Standards Scientific Papers,* Vol. 15, 1918–1920, pp. 101–104, (Scientific Paper 336).

---

[4] The ferrite that forms in steels containing a little less than 0.80% carbon may also collect in the grain boundaries at some rates of cooling.

3. B. A. Rogers and K. O. Stamm: "A Magnetic Determination of the A₃ Transformation Point in Iron," *Transactions,* American Institute of Mining and Metallurgical Engineers, Vol. 150, 1942, pp. 131–141.
4. Francis F. Lucas: "On the Art of Metallography," *Transactions,* American Institute of Mining and Metallurgical Engineers, Vol. 95, 1931, pp. 11–44.

CHAPTER 10

The Hardening of Steel

THE BEGINNING OF THIS CHAPTER is a convenient point for the clearing away of some confusion for which writers of fiction appear to be partly responsible. In their desire to emphasize strength of body or of character, these writers have used expressions like, "as hard as tempered steel" or "as strong as tempered steel." These phrases imply that tempering is a hardening process, whereas, it actually is a softening or ameliorating process. Sterne used the word correctly in his "God tempers the wind to the shorn lamb." Metallurgists use the word tempering to mean a softening process for reducing the brittleness of quenched steel at some sacrifice of hardness and strength.

Steel that has been treated to produce structures like those shown in the photomicrographs of Chapter 9 is of little value as a cutting tool although it is useful for other purposes. To be hardened, steel must be cooled very rapidly.

Only slightly higher rates of cooling than those of the previous chapter decrease the thickness of the laminae of iron and iron carbide and increase their number correspondingly. With yet more rapid cooling, the plates

[150]

become so thin and so numerous as to be unresolvable, or indistinguishable, with the best optical microscopes. An electron microscope can follow the changing character of the laminae much farther as may be noted in

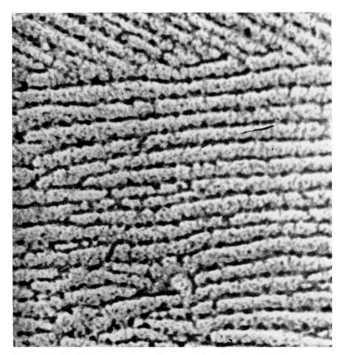

Fig. 10.1 Thin Laminae Formed by Faster Cooling

This photomicrograph shows the decrease in thickness of the alternate plates of iron (light) and iron carbide (dark) that form when the rate of cooling of the specimen is increased moderately as compared with the rates of the previous chapter. The plates are spaced so closely that they could not be seen at all with an optical microscope, yet they stand out clearly in this picture taken with an electron microscope.

Courtesy, C. S. Barrett, Institute for the Study of Metals.

Magnification, 20,000×

Fig. 10.1 which shows, at 20,000 diameters, a piece of steel so treated as to produce fine laminae.

THE HARDENING TRANSFORMATION

Increased rates of cooling yield new types of structure in a steel as becomes evident upon examination of polished sections under a microscope. To get a structure that will make steel hard enough to be useful as a cutting tool, one must use high rates of cooling. The cooling must be so rapid that the carbon atoms do not have time to move out of the positions they occupy in the high-temperature form (austenite) before the steel becomes so rigid that they are unable to move. The holding of the atoms in place does not mean that no transformation occurs. Rather, it means that the product is not the same as when transformation takes place at a slower rate of cooling. The product of fast cooling is a supersaturated solid solution, that is, much more carbon is in "solution" than is normal for room temperature. The arrangement of atoms in this solution may be described most satisfactorily as body-centered tetragonal. Carbon atoms appear to be in the interstices as in austenite. Hence, the structure is much different from the composite of alternate layers of iron and iron carbide described above. When examined microscopically, a steel that has been cooled rapidly is found to have a characteristic acicular or needlelike structure like that in Fig. 10.2. This typical structure is called "martensite."

THE ISOTHERMAL TRANSFORMATION CURVE

The previous paragraph emphasized the need for rapid cooling if the steel were to have a structure satisfactory for a good cutting tool. It did not, however, give details concerning the need for rapid cooling. An understanding of the rate-of-cooling problem may be gained from a study of a type of curve known as an "isothermal transformation" curve or, sometimes, as a "time-temperature-transformation" curve. Such a curve represents the results of an entire series of experiments on one particular composition of steel. A curve for a "plain carbon" steel containing 0.90% carbon is presented in Fig. 10.3. This composition is sufficiently near the point S of Fig. 9.7 that the steel is described as being of eutectoid composition. The isothermal transformation curve actually

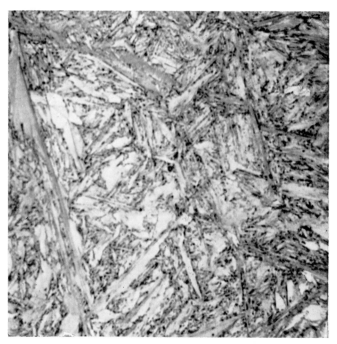

Fig. 10.2   Microscopic Appearance of Hardened Steel

The articular, or needlelike, structure shown in this figure is characteristic of etched sections of hardened steel. This structure is called *martensite*. It is produced only if the transformation takes place at low temperature.

Vilella, Guellich and Bain (*1*).   Magnification, 2000×

is a combination of two associated curves, one that corresponds to the beginning of transformation and the other related to its ending.

The data needed for preparing such a graph are obtained by the quenching of a set of small pieces of steel in the austenitic condition, that is, from above the transformation, into a large volume of quenching medium maintained at a selected temperature. The length of time each specimen was kept in the medium was determined accurately. At the end of its period, each specimen was quenched immediately to room temperature and examined microscopically. (Areas that had been altered while the specimen was in the medium could be distinguished from areas changed during the final quenching.) As would be expected, specimens were found to contain less austenite and more transformation product the longer they had been in the medium. From microscopic examination of the set of specimens, the experimenter could determine which one showed the beginning and which the end of the transformation. The intervals that these two specimens had been immersed were then plotted against the temperature of the medium.

A casual examination of Fig. 10.3 reveals that the time required for the transformation to start after the specimen has been immersed varies greatly with temperature. For a temperature slightly under 720°C., the interval before transformation begins may be an hour or more. It decreases rapidly as the temperature of the medium diminishes until, at 550°C., it is less than one second. Further lowering of the temperature causes the interval to lengthen. At 300°C., about 2 minutes are required for the transforming action to begin. At 230°C., the specimen begins to transform by a different mechanism to be described shortly, and the product is martensite.

Obviously the problem of quenching a steel with suf-

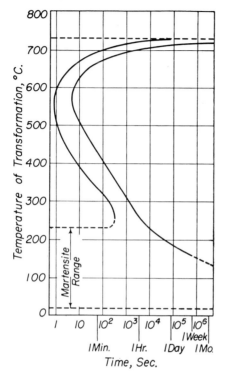

Fig. 10.3 Isothermal Transformation Curve

This isothermal transformation curve is for a 0.90% carbon steel. The "curve" is really a pair of curves. The left one indicates the number of seconds before transformation begins in a specimen suddenly immersed in a liquid at the temperature specified. The right curve gives the number of seconds from immersion to complete conversion at that temperature. The horizontal distance between them gives the time required for transformation. The upper portion of this graph was taken from an article in *Metals and Alloys* (2), the lower part was drawn in by the author in accordance with the ideas of Grange and Stewart (3) and Professor Cohen's discussion of Greninger and Troiano (4).

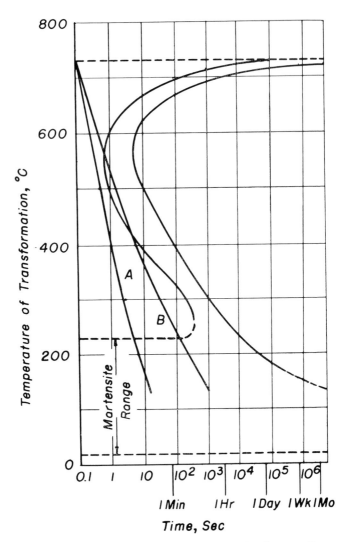

Fig. 10.4 Cooling Rate Necessary To Produce a Completely Martensitic Structure

A specimen that cools along the temperature-time path marked *A* will be purely martensitic. One that follows path *B* almost certainly will undergo some conversion to pearlite in the vicinity of 500°C.

ficient rapidity to produce a purely martensitic structure reduces to the problem of cooling it so rapidly that no transformation occurs in the vicinity of 500°C. to 600°C. What must be done may be understood from Fig. 10.4. This figure shows the isothermal transformation curve of Fig. 10.3 replotted on a graph of which the time scale has been extended leftward to 0.1 second. Also, curves *A* and *B* have been added. They trace the decrease in temperature with time of two specimens. The specimen that cooled with the rapidity indicated by curve *A* reached 230°C. without undergoing any transformation at higher temperature. It was ultimately converted entirely to martensite. The specimen that followed path *B* was subject to transformation in the part of the path that lies across the "nose" or "knee" of the isothermal curve. A photomicrograph of a specimen in which some transformation occurred in the 500°C. to 600°C. interval is shown in Fig. 10.5. The dark wide portions of the grain boundary and the patches that straddle the grain boundaries are fine pearlite that formed at the temperature of the nose. The interior portions of the grains are martensite. Transformations, characteristically, start at grain boundaries.

TRANSFORMATION TO MARTENSITE DEPENDS ON TEMPERATURE ONLY

On Fig. 10.3 is an interval of temperature marked "Martensite Range," meaning that the formation of martensite begins at the upper limit and is completed at the lower limit. The significance of this range is that the austenite-martensite transformation does not proceed with time but only as the temperature is lowered. The evidence for this behavior is contained in the next three photomicrographs. Figure 10.6 shows a piece of steel of 1.08% carbon content that has been quenched into a medium at 140°C. and held there for one second. The extent of transformation is indicated by the dark, needle-

Fig. 10.5 Iron-Carbon Alloy Transformed in Two Steps

The rate of cooling was sufficiently low to permit some conversion in the vicinity of 500°C. to 600°C. As the piece cooled below this range, the reaction ceased. Continued cooling brought the specimen into the interval of the low temperature reaction and the remaining austenite was changed to martensite. The tendency for the high-temperature transformation to begin along the grain boundaries is obvious. Because of a different etching procedure the martensite portion of this photomicrograph appears as a very light constituent instead of being dark as in the other figures.

Digges (5). Magnification, 100×

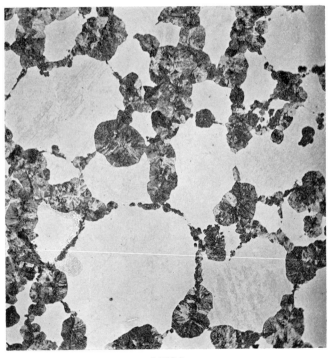

Fig. 10.6   Martensite Transformation—Early Stage

This specimen of 1.08% carbon steel was cooled rapidly to 140°C. and held at that temperature for one second. The dark needles indicate the portion which transformed during this interval and the white background shows the portion which did not.

Greninger and Troiano (4).   Magnification, 500×

shaped areas. White material remained as austenite after the one second interval. If the temperature of the medium is reduced to 100°C., the transforming effect is much greater as indicated by Fig. 10.7. The specimen was held, in this instance also, for one second. However,

Fig. 10.7   Martensite Formation—Intermediate Stage

This figure shows the same steel that was illustrated in Fig. 10.6 treated in the same manner except that the temperature of the bath was 100°C. instead of 140°C. The increased percentage of conversion is the more easily estimated because both pictures were taken at the same magnification.

Greninger and Troiano (4).   Magnification, 500×

Fig. 10.8   Martensite Formation—Intermediate Stage

This is the same steel as in the previous figure after being held
in the quenching bath at 100°C. for 100 days instead of one
second. The reader will note how little is the difference in
appearance between the two specimens. At this temperature,
time appears to be of minor importance.

Courtesy, A. R. Troiano, Department of Metallurgy, Case Institute of Technology.   Magnification, 500×

---

the time at temperature turns out to be immaterial as
the same result was obtained (Fig. 10.8) whether the specimen was held at 100°C. for one second or for 100 days.

EFFECT OF CARBON ON THE MARTENSITE RANGE

The specimens of the three previous figures all contained 1.08% carbon. Hence, they should not be expected to have the same martensite range as the 0.90% carbon steel of Fig. 10.3. Experiments have shown that the temperature at which the austenite-martensite transformation begins does vary with carbon content and, more definitely, that it is lowered if the percentage of carbon is increased. The trend is shown in Fig. 10.9.

EFFECT OF RATE OF COOLING

Not only does the martensite range vary with carbon content but so also does the rate of cooling necessary to produce a completely martensitic structure. For a set of

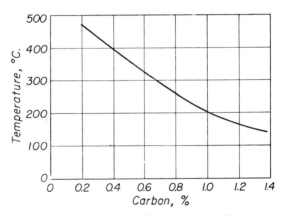

Fig.10.9   Temperature of Formation of Martensite

This curve indicates the beginning of the austenite-martensite transformation. The reaction is completed at much lower temperatures. This graph represents laboratory alloys and lies at slightly higher temperatures than the corresponding one for commercial steels. It has been redrawn from Greninger *(6)*.

Fig. 10.10   Influence of Carbon on Critical Cooling Rate

This curve indicates the rate at which iron-carbon alloys must be cooled through the range 500°C. to 600°C., in order that no transformation shall occur in that interval of temperature. The equivalent curve for a commercial steel would lie considerably below this one because other elements always present in these steels reduce the critical rate. In general, alloying elements reduce the critical cooling rate markedly. Also, the size of the grains in the steel before it is quenched has some influence. This graph was redrawn from Digges (7).

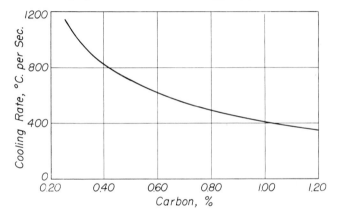

laboratory-made specimens that were essentially simple iron-carbon alloys,[1] the required rate of cooling depends on carbon content in the manner depicted in Fig. 10.10. A similar graph for a commercial steel would lie consid-

---

[1] Even the most carefully made commercial steels contain small amounts of several elements besides carbon. Certain to be present are sulfur, phosphorus, silicon, and manganese. Not all of these elements are necessarily undesirable. In particular, silicon and manganese often are adjusted to produce specific properties in a steel. In recent years, other elements, such as copper, chromium, and molybdenum are likely to be introduced from the scrap used in making the steel. As a result, the manufacture of even a "plain carbon steel" is a complicated process.

erably below the one shown in this figure. This means that the rates of cooling required for conversion to a completely martensitic structure would be lower for all carbon contents. By how much the curve is lowered depends on the percentages of other elements than carbon.

An obvious connection exists between the position of the curve in Fig. 10.10 and the position of the nose (Fig. 10.4) of the isothermal transformation curves of the corresponding steels. As alloying elements almost always cause the nose to move to the right regardless of carbon content, they have the effect of decreasing the rate of cooling needed to get the steel through the 500°C.–600°C. range without transformation. This decrease in required rate of cooling means a lowering of the curve illustrated in Fig. 10.10.

BAINITE

As yet, no comment has been made about the nature of the transformation in the interval extending from the temperature at which fine pearlite is formed down to the temperature at which martensite begins to appear. On the isothermal transformation curve (Fig. 10.3), this interval extends from a bit below the nose down to the upper boundary of the martensite range—commonly called "M_s." Over this interval, the product of this transformation as viewed through a microscope resembles neither pearlite nor martensite. A feature that the product frequently does show when examined microscopically is a feathery appearance along the grain boundaries, the boundaries themselves serving as shafts for the "feathers." Interior areas of the grains often appear indistinct. The higher magnifications obtainable with an electron microscope show that the barbs of the feathers are strings of elongated iron carbide particles imbedded in a ferrite matrix as illustrated in Fig. 10.11. This new structure, called "bainite," character-

Fig. 10.11   The Structure of Bainite as Revealed by the Electron Microscope

At high magnification, bainite is seen to be composed of cementite particles distributed through a ferrite background. In this figure the formation of bainite is just getting under way. Barbs, or needles, of bainite are extending themselves out into the austenitic region.

Courtesy of Research Laboratories, General Motors Corporation.   Magnification, 7000×, reduced by ⅓ in reproduction

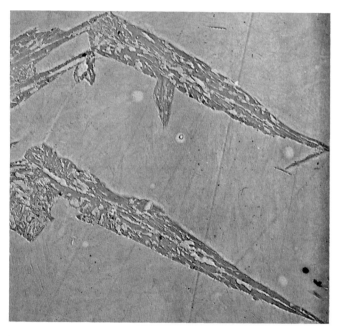

istically appears as strings of carbide particles running in different directions. Obviously, a major difference between bainite and pearlite is that in the former, the striae are broken up into individual particles. Actually, Fig. 10.11 shows bainite in a beginning stage of formation. The barb of a feather is extending out into surrounding (untransformed) austenite. As the transformation continues, the entire area shown will be converted to carbide particles imbedded in ferrite.

Some differences in character exist between the product of transformation at a temperature not far below

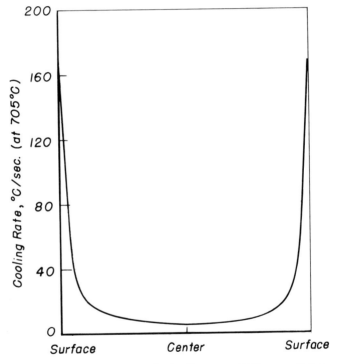

Fig. 10.12   The Rate of Cooling at Different Points Along the Diameter of a Quenched 4-inch Round Bar

This curve is for a bar quenched in mildly agitated water. This type of quench could be considered to be of about average severity.

the knee of the time-temperature-transformation curve (Fig. 10.3) and the structure formed a bit above the M_s line (230°C. in Fig. 10.3) but both are called bainite. The specimen in Fig. 10.11 represents "upper bainite."

THE QUENCHING OF LARGE BARS

The requirement that a piece of steel cool faster than some limiting rate if it is to become entirely martensitic when it has been quenched brings up the question of what happens in the interior of a large mass of steel. Obviously, the heat from the interior of, for example, a 4-inch diameter round bar cannot escape as rapidly as it can from the exterior of the bar; hence, the temperature of the interior cannot drop as rapidly. How much the rate of cooling decreases from the surface to the center of a 4-inch bar is evident from Fig. 10.12. From the figure, one can see that if the bar is made of a kind of steel that must be cooled at 100°C. per second or faster for the formation of martensite, only the outside rim of the bar will be hardened fully. This problem of a hard rim and a soft core exists for relatively small bars. An illustration of the situation in a 1-inch bar is given in Fig. 10.13. That only a narrow rim is hard is evident both from the differences in etching between the inner and outer portions (Fig. 10.13A) and from the variation in hardness along a diameter (Fig. 10.13B).

HARDENABILITY

For a specific type of quenching, the depth to which a bar of steel will harden depends upon its composition as well as its size. A hint concerning the effect of composition was given in the section on "Effect of Rate of Cooling." If the composition of the steel is such that a high rate of cooling is necessary for full hardening, only the outer portion will be hard. On the other hand, if

Fig. 10.13A   Cross Section of Quenched Steel Bar

This figure illustrates the cross section of a 1-inch diameter plain carbon steel bar after quenching. Only the metal near the surface cooled with sufficient rapidity to escape transformation in the 500°C. to 600°C. range of temperature. Consequently, only the exterior of the bar was hardened. Since the etching reagent darkened only the hardened area, one may estimate roughly the depth of hardening by the width of the dark band. Courtesy, G. V. Luerssen, Carpenter Steel Co.

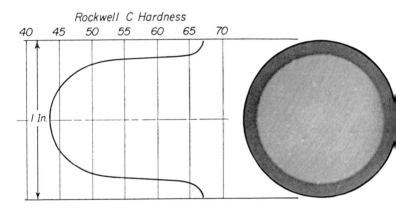

Fig. 10.13B   Variation in Hardness of Quenched Steel Bar

Measurements of hardness along a diameter of a bar like the one shown in Fig. 10.13A indicate clearly the relative softness of the central portion. The hardness decreases rapidly at the junction of the dark rim and light core. Alloying elements or an increase in the high-temperature grain size of the steel would lift the depressed center of this graph.

---

the steel will harden for a relatively low rate of cooling, the entire cross section may be hard. Steel of the first type—narrow hard rim and soft center—is called a "shallow hardening" steel. Steel of the second type is described as "deep hardening." The characteristic of being shallow hardening or deep hardening is called the "hardenability" of the steel.

Addition of alloying elements may so reduce the rate of cooling necessary to obtain a completely martensitic structure that even the slowly cooled center of a large bar may be fully hardened.[2] An example of such a steel is given in Fig. 10.14. Essentially what alloying does is to lower the curve of the required rate of cooling (Fig. 10.10) as described above and thereby increase the depth of hardening.

Although the control of composition and the establishment of a definite grain size permit prediction of hardenability—depth of hardening under specific quenching conditions—they do not do so with exactness. For this reason, tests of hardenability often are made on samples from a shipment of steel before the steel is started into production of parts. In some instances, a statement of hardenability is considered part of the specifications. The extent to which hardenability can vary in steels is illustrated by the group of steels in Fig. 10.15. These 1-inch bars have been put in the order of their depth of hardening.

TEMPERING

Because steel is brittle in the merely quenched condition, it is almost never used in that state.[3] Its ductility can be improved greatly if it is heated to a relatively low temperature for a short time. Some reduction in

---

[2] The size of the grains of austenite existing in the steel prior to the quenching operation also has a considerable influence on the depth to which a piece of steel will harden under a particular heat treatment. In turn, the size of the austenite grains is related to composition, temperature at the time of quenching, and apparently, in some degree upon the hard-to-define melting practice.

[3] This statement does not hold for steel parts with carburized and hardened surfaces. In many instances, a high surface hardness is desirable and is metallurgically acceptable because of the relatively soft interior which supports the hardened face.

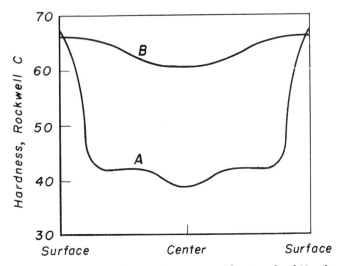

Fig. 10.14   The Effect of Alloying on the Depth of Hardening

Curve *A* shows the hardness across a diameter of a round bar of plain carbon steel containing about 0.75% carbon content. Curve *B* gives the hardness across a diameter of a bar of about the same carbon content but with nickel and chromium added. Both bars were 1⅝ inch in diameter. The softness of the central portion of the plain carbon steel bar is obvious. On the other hand, the alloyed bar has been hardened in the interior almost as much as at the surface.
Modified from a graph by Bain *(8)*.

strength and hardness is not considered too high a price to pay for this advantage.

The softening that occurs when a steel is reheated, or tempered, takes place with astonishing speed in the initial stage. The 0.82% carbon steel on which Fig. 10.16 is based softened more in the first minute at 535°C. than in the next 25 hours. Accordingly, one may believe that

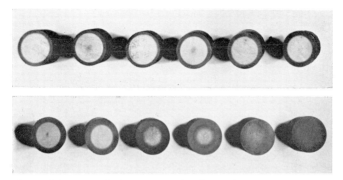

Fig. 10.15   Variation in Depth of Hardening

This figure depicts a group of 1-inch diameter plain carbon toolsteel bars, all of the same nominal composition, after being heated and quenched according to a fixed procedure. The bars are arranged in order of their depth of hardening, or *hardenability*. The bar at the upper left hardened only a short distance below the surface whereas the one at the lower right hardened completely through. The specimen at the top left is known as *shallow hardening* and that at the bottom right as *deep hardening*.
Courtesy, B. F. Shepherd, Ingersoll-Rand Co.

---

quenched steel is in a highly abnormal condition as compared with what might be considered its equilibrium state.

The changes that take place when tempering begins in a quenched steel are known in a general way. The first event is the movement of carbon atoms from the positions in which they were caught by the quenching operation, that is, very nearly the same position that they occupied in the austenite. Simultaneously with this movement the carbon atoms unite chemically with some iron atoms to form a carbide having the formula Fe_2C, or, at least, a compound containing less iron than the customary Fe_3C. Not all of the carbon atoms come out immediately; enough remain so that the iron constituent

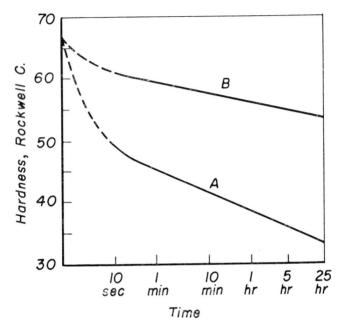

Fig. 10.16   The Softening of Quenched Steel by Tempering

Curve *A* is for specimens held at 535°C. for the times indicated below the graph. Curve *B* is for specimens held at 315°C. Specimens held at 535°C. softened by a greater number of hardness points during the first minute than during the ensuing 25 hours. The specimens were from a steel containing 0.82% carbon and 0.75% manganese.

Modified from a graph by Bain (8).

contains about 0.3%. Hence, the partially tempered steel is still considered to be martensite. However, a consequence of the reduction in carbon content is that the martensite changes from the tetragonal structure that it had immediately after quenching to a normal body-centered cubic structure. This initial action takes place slowly at the temperature of boiling water and becomes rapid at 200°C.

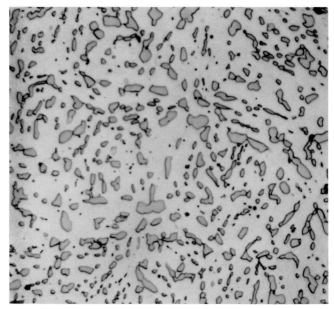

Fig. 10.17   Steel That Has Been Quenched and Then Tempered at a High Temperature

Obviously, the tempering temperature was not high enough to cause any conversion to austenite. The particles of carbide (cementite) dispersed throughout the ferrite background are the result of the agglomeration of the tiny particles precipitated from the martensite during the initial stages of tempering. Particles of carbide of this type frequently are called "spheroidal cementite" and the structure as a whole is called "spheroidite."

Courtesy of Research Laboratory, U.S. Steel Corporation.

Magnification, 2000×

At a higher temperature, further action takes place. The martensite loses nearly all of its carbon and is converted to alpha iron. Also, the Fe_2C disappears and Fe_3C forms. In this stage, the particles of carbide (cementite) become microscopically visible. Continued heating to higher temperatures results in growth, or agglomeration, of the carbide particles into microscopically visible sizes such as those in Fig. 10.17. These rounded particles often are called "spheroidal cementite" and the structure as a whole is known as "spheroidite."

THE IMPORTANCE OF THE IRON-CARBON ALLOYS

Obviously, only a very small fraction of the known facts about the iron-carbon alloy system has been covered in these two chapters. In fact, only the barest outline was given of the part that was included—mainly plain carbon steels. Very little was said about alloy steels. Nothing at all has been included concerning the different kinds of cast irons that are produced if the carbon content is increased. The iron-carbon system is the subject of numerous publications and one cannot expect to be familiar with more than a small proportion of them.

REFERENCES

1. J. R. Vilella, G. E. Guellich and E. C. Bain: "On Naming the Aggregate Constituents in Steel," *Transactions,* American Society for Metals, Vol. 24, 1936, pp. 225–252.

2. "The Process and Result of Austenite Formation at Constant Temperature," *Metals and Alloys,* Vol. 8, 1937, pp. 22–24.

3. R. A. Grange and H. M. Stewart: "The Temperature Range of Martensite Formation," *Transactions,* American Institute of Mining and Metallurgical Engineers, Vol. 167, 1946, pp. 467–490.

4. Alden B. Greninger and Alexander R. Troiano: "Kinetics of the Austenite to Martensite Transformation in Steel,"

Transactions, American Society for Metals, Vol. 28, 1940, pp. 537–563.

5. Thomas G. Digges: "Transformation of Austenite on Quenching High Purity Iron-Carbon Alloys," *Transactions,* American Society for Metals, Vol. 28, 1940, pp. 575–600.

6. Alden B. Greninger: "The Martensite Thermal Arrest in Iron-Carbon Alloys and Plain Carbon Steels," *Transactions,* American Society for Metals, Vol. 30, 1942, pp. 1–26.

7. Thomas G. Digges: "Effect of Carbon on the Hardenability of High Purity Iron-Carbon Alloys," *Transactions,* American Society for Metals, Vol. 26, 1938, pp. 408–421.

8. Edgar C. Bain: "Functions of the Alloying Elements in Steel," American Society for Metals, Cleveland, 1939. Graph for Fig. 10.5 is on page 181. Graph for Fig. 10.7 is on page 233.

9. B. S. Lement, B. L. Averbach, and Morris Cohen: "Microstructural Changes on Tempering Iron-Carbon Alloys," *Transactions,* American Society for Metals, Vol. 46, 1954, pp. 851–877.

10. B. S. Lement, B. L. Averbach, and Morris Cohen: "Further Study of Microstructural Changes on Tempering Iron-Carbon Alloys," *Transactions,* American Society for Metals, Vol. 47, 1955, pp. 291–313.

CHAPTER 11

Alloy Diagrams

SEVERAL DESCRIPTIONS of alloys presented in this book have been based on a type of diagram frequently referred to simply as an "alloy diagram." More formally, they are known as "constitutional diagrams," "phase diagrams," or "equilibrium diagrams." An example was the copper-nickel diagram of Fig. 4.4, which is the simplest type known. It represents all of the possible alloys of these two metals. In particular, it indicates, for any composition, at what temperatures the alloy is solid, at what temperatures it is liquid and at what temperatures it is partly solid, and partly liquid.

Examples of a second, and very common, type of diagram are the lead-tin diagram shown in Fig. 5.2 and the copper-silver diagram of Fig. 5.8. These diagrams are described as "simple eutectic" diagrams because of the one eutectic point (B) to be found in them. A variant of the same type is the cadmium-bismuth diagram of Fig. 5.7. This diagram differs from the other two in that lines such as AD have moved to the borders of the diagram because neither element is noticeably soluble in the other instead of having a limited solubility as in the lead-tin and copper-silver systems.

Diagrams like those mentioned above and other, more complicated ones are important in metallurgy. Accordingly, this chapter will be devoted to a few examples.

ATOMIC PERCENTAGES

In the diagrams that have been presented, the compositions shown along the base line indicate the proportion of the second metal as a per cent of the weight of the total mass of alloy. Frequently, compositions are expressed as the percentage of the total number of atoms contributed by the second element. Usually, these two ways of specifying composition are called "weight per cent" and "atomic per cent." A still shorter designation is w/o and a/o. The relation between the two may be formulated as

$$\text{w/o of } B = \frac{(\text{a/o of } B)\ (\text{at. wt. of } B)}{(\text{a/o of } B)\ (\text{at. wt. of } B)\ +\ (\text{a/o of } A)\ (\text{at. wt. of } A)} \times 100$$

$$\text{a/o of } B = \frac{\dfrac{\text{w/o of } B}{\text{at. wt. of } B}}{\dfrac{\text{w/o of } B}{\text{at. wt. of } B}\ +\ \dfrac{\text{w/o of } A}{\text{at. wt. of } A}} \times 100$$

Calculation of the weight per cent of lead in the compound Mg_2Pb will serve as an example of the usefulness of these expressions. The atomic per cent of lead in this compound must be 33.33 since one of the three atoms in a molecule is lead. Substitution of this atomic percentage and the atomic weights of the two metals in the first of the above equations yields a weight per cent of lead of 80.99.

A PERITECTIC SITUATION

A glance at the zirconium-vanadium diagram in Fig. 11.1[1] shows that it contains a eutectic arrangement of lines indicated by *ABF* and *DBE* that resembles corresponding lines in Fig. 5.2 and Fig. 5.7. In addition to this familiar feature, the diagram contains the combination *FGH* and *MEG*. An arrangement of this kind has a significance that will be understood if one follows the process of solidification of an alloy of composition *x*.

Alloy *x* begins to solidify about 1570°C. by the formation of solid solution, or δ phase, of composition *z*. Upon further cooling, more solid is formed with the result that the composition of liquid follows along *CF* to *F* and that of the solid, simultaneously, along *CH* to *H*. At the temperature of *FGH* an unexpected event occurs. All of the remaining liquid reacts with part of the solid, δ, to produce a compound of the composition *MEG* specified as γ phase[2] in the diagram. This reaction is a "peritectic reaction." It completes itself at a fixed temperature *FGH*—about 1300°C. At its end, the alloy consists of two solid phases, compound γ having composition *G* and solid solution δ of composition *H*. The relative amounts of the two substances may be calculated by the law of levers set down in Chapter 5 as the law holds regardless of whether the phases are solid or liquid. At a temperature slightly below *FGH,* the compound constitutes about 60 w/o of the alloy.

---

[1] In the figure from which Fig. 11.1 was copied [see Williams *(1)*] several lines, for example *BFC*, were dotted to indicate that their positions were not known exactly. Other figures in this chapter were taken from original diagrams in which one or more lines were dotted. However, for the purpose of illustrating a type of diagram, some uncertainty about the position of a line is inconsequential. Accordingly, all diagrams in this chapter have been drawn with full lines. Before making practical use of a diagram, the reader should consult the publication in which it appeared originally.

[2] Phase may be loosely defined as substance or material but see Appendix.

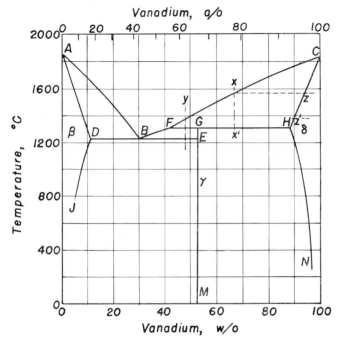

Fig. 11.1 An Incomplete Zirconium-Vanadium Alloy Diagram

This diagram is intended to aid in an explanation of the peritectic reaction in this system. A part of the diagram not needed for this purpose has been omitted. All alloys that have compositions between F and H undergo a peritectic reaction upon solidifying. As the alloy reaches the temperature FGH, liquid of composition F and solid of composition H react to produce a compound of composition G (γ phase). If the alloy has the composition x, some δ will remain unreacted so that below FGH the alloy consists of the two phases γ and δ. Williams *(1)*.

An alloy of composition y begins to solidify about 1380°C. by forming δ substance of composition z'. When it goes through the peritectic reaction, all of the δ substance is consumed in producing γ compound but some liquid is left over. Upon continued cooling, this liquid rejects additional γ phase and, consequently changes in composition along FB. As it reaches temperature DBE, it solidifies completely by a eutectic reaction.

Peritectic reaction in an alloy of composition G should yield only the compound γ. That it does so is apparent from Fig. 11.2 which shows the microscopically homo-

Fig. 11.2   Photomicrograph of the Compound ZrV$_2$

This photomicrograph indicates the homogeneous character of the alloy containing 53% vanadium. It appears to be completely single phase although it contains about 0.2% vanadium in excess of the theoretical percentage for the compound. The triangular markings are related to the crystalline structure of the compound and do not indicate a second phase.

Williams *(1)*.   Magnification, 680×

geneous compound. The triangular markings indicate only a peculiarity of inner structure. A second phase, if present, would appear as tiny particles distributed throughout the compound. One notes from the scale of atomic percentages along the top of Fig. 11.1 that the compound γ appears at about 67% vanadium, corresponding to the formula ZrV_2.

EFFECT OF FAST COOLING

A homogeneous compound like the one shown in Fig. 11.2 is not easy to obtain even by very slow cooling. Rapid cooling produces the very inhomogeneous alloy shown in Fig. 11.3. What happened here was that the reaction between the particles of δ substance and the surounding liquid, approximately of composition F, formed envelopes of γ material around the particles. Consequently, contact between the two reacting substances was cut off and the peritectic reaction could proceed only as atoms diffused through the envelopes. In Fig. 11.3, the gray particles are δ phase and the white envelopes surrounding them are γ phase formed during the reaction. The dark regions were still liquid at the end of the peritectic reaction.

PERITECTIC REACTION MAY NOT YIELD A COMPOUND

A peritectic reaction may produce a compound as in the zirconium-vanadium system but it may also yield a solid solution. An example of the second type of result may be seen by referring back to Fig. 5.11 which shows that no less than 5 peritectic reactions appear in the copper-zinc alloys and all of them produce solid solutions.

TWO WAYS OF FORMING COMPOUNDS

Figure 5.10 and Fig. 11.1 illustrate two ways in which compounds form during solidification. In the magne-

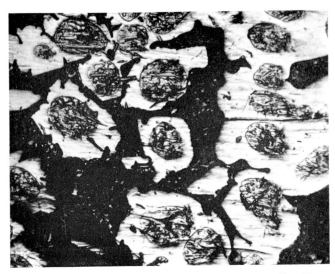

Fig. 11.3 The Effect of Rapid Cooling on an Alloy Having the Proportions of ZrV$_2$

This alloy should appear as in Fig. 11.2 but rapid cooling has left it so far out of equilibrium that three phases are present. The gray particles are δ phase. Surrounding them are lighter colored envelopes of γ phase (compound). The black material was liquid at the peritectic temperature, line *FGH*.
Williams *(1)*.   Magnification, 1200×

sium-lead system, the compound PbMg$_2$ is formed by solidification directly from the melt. Also, the solid compound melts completely at one temperature to liquid. On the other hand, the compound γ in the zirconium-vanadium system does not come into existence until solidification is well under way, that is, until the peritectic reaction sets in. In the reverse sense, the compound does not melt directly to liquid but dissociates at some temperature into liquid plus a solid of different composition.

THE MONOTECTIC REACTION

As mentioned in Chapter 4, two metals may be totally or partially immiscible even in the liquid state. The copper-lead system for which the diagram is shown in Fig. 11.4 is an illustration of partial, or limited, solubility. As in most instances of this kind, the degree of miscibility depends on temperature. Figure 11.4 shows that above about 1000°C., complete miscibility exists but that at lower temperatures a separation into two liquids takes place. In the 65% lead alloy, the two layers form at 990°C. Continued cooling causes one layer to become higher in lead content and the other to lose lead. Naturally, the copper contents change in the opposite direction. Upon reaching 953°C., the upper layer designated as L_1 undergoes a reaction much like a eutectic solidification except that one of the new substances is a liquid (L_2). Because one of the substances is a liquid the event is described as a "monotectic reaction."

The result of the monotectic reaction that occurs in a 53.6% lead alloy is shown in Fig. 11.5. As the photomicrograph suggests, the upper layer has been converted to a porous mass of copper with liquid L_2 filling the pores. The liquid in the pores solidifies upon further cooling in the same manner as the liquid L_2 that constitutes the lower layer. As L_2 continues to cool, it rejects copper down to 326°C. At this temperature solidification is completed by a eutectic reaction that cannot be indicated on Fig. 10.4 because the eutectic point is too close to the right boundary.

ALLOTROPIC TRANSFORMATIONS COMPLICATE ALLOY DIAGRAMS

The A_3 transformation in iron was described in Chapter 9. Transformations in metals are not uncommon. For example, transformations in the close-packed hexagonal metals zirconium and titanium cause both to become body-centered cubic at elevated temperature, the first at

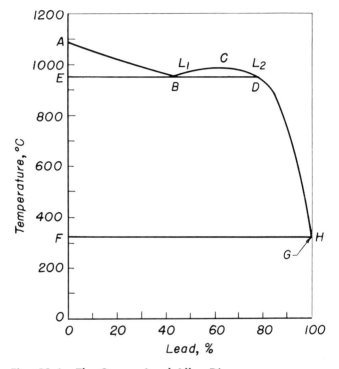

Fig. 11.4 The Copper-Lead Alloy Diagram

This diagram is interesting because it shows a liquid alloy breaking up into two other liquid alloys of different composition. One result of this behavior is the monotectic reaction in which a liquid alloy breaks up into a solid plus a liquid of different composition than the decomposing one.

This diagram is based on one given in the *Metals Handbook* (2) but has been modified in accordance with results published by Pelzel (3).

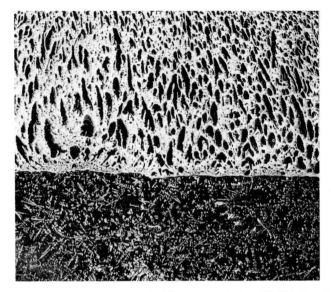

Fig. 11.5   A Copper-Lead Alloy Containing 53.6% Lead

This photomicrograph shows the two portions that resulted from the separation of the liquid alloy into two layers. The lower area represents the liquid layer that contained the most lead. The small dendrites of copper in this area were precipitated from the liquid L_2 as it cooled from D to G (Fig. 11.4). Pelzel (3).   Magnification, 10×

865°C. and the second at 885°C. Some metals have more than one transformation. Iron and uranium each have two, manganese has three and plutonium has five. In some instances, transformations provide a means of attaining valuable properties by heat treatment. In all cases, they introduce additional lines into alloy diagrams.

HOW TRANSFORMATIONS ALTER DIAGRAMS

A transformation in one of the components of an alloy
shows in the diagram as a point from which two lines
extend. Both of the lines either ascend or descend. One
does not ascend and the other descend. In the titanium-
vanadium diagram given in Fig. 11.6 both lines descend
toward room temperature.

Eutectoid Situations

A situation like that depicted in Fig. 11.6 is unusual.
In most instances, the two lines continue until the upper
one strikes another line such as a solvus line (Chapter

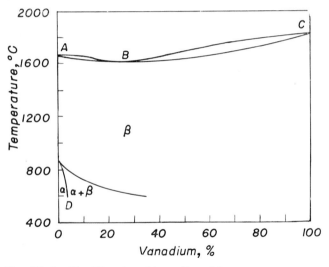

Fig. 11.6   The Titanium-Vanadium Diagram

This simple diagram illustrates the effect on a phase diagram
of a transformation in one of the component metals. In this
case, the two lines extending out from the transformation in
titanium simply continue toward room temperature.
Adenstedt, Pequignot, and Raymer *(4)*.

8). An example of this situation was seen in the partial iron-carbon diagram shown in Fig. 9.7. Here, the line *GS* coming from the transformation point *G* intersected the solvus line *ES* at *S*. Another result of the intersection was the formation of the horizontal line *PS* terminating

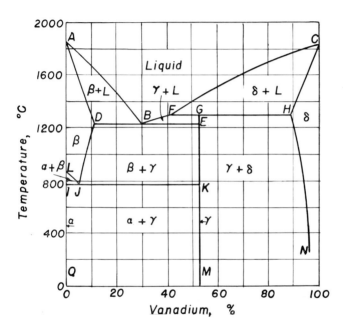

Fig. 11.7   The   Complete   Zirconium-Vanadium   Alloy Diagram

In this figure, the lines *LJ* and *IJK* related to the transformation in zirconium have been added. Line *LIQ* also has its origin in this transformation but because zirconium will not take any vanadium into solid solution, it lies so close to the left side that it coincides with the zero coordinate.

This figure has been modified slightly from one published by Williams (*1*).

at the left where it meets the lower of the lines from G and at the right on some other line.

A similar situation may be seen in Fig. 11.7. This diagram is complete and shows the lines due to the transformation in zirconium that were omitted from Fig. 11.1. Line LJ originating at the transformation point L intersects the solvus line JD at J. The horizontal formed is IJK. It intersects the lower of the lines from L at I. However I has vanished into the left boundary because of the very low solubility of vanadium in α zirconium.

On account of the similarity in the positions of LJD and IJK to a eutectic situation, point J is called a "eutectoid" point. In the iron-carbon diagram, S is a eutectoid point.

Peritectoid Situations

An example of ascending lines is shown in Fig. 11.8. Here the upper of the lines coming from the transformation in titanium strikes the solvus line LE at E. The resulting horizontal line extends to the right from E. The lower of the lines from K is stopped by the horizontal and "bounces" back toward room temperature. The similarity of this arrangement to the peritectic situation has led to the name "peritectoid point" for point F.

Although the above way of describing lines introduced as the result of transformations is useful, the real meaning of the horizontal line EFG is that at this temperature, a cooling alloy containing, for example, 33% aluminum will undergo a peritectoid reaction as the result of which α phase will be formed.

Monotectoid Situations

The monotectic type of diagram has its counterpart also. Solid solutions may decompose into two similar solid solutions of different composition. The effect in the alloy diagram is to introduce a "miscibility gap" or "decomposition loop." The gold-nickel system contains

Fig. 11.8   The Titanium-Aluminum Diagram

In this diagram, the lines extending out from the transformation turn upward until the upper one meets a solvus line coming down from the peritectic horizontal at 1460°C. As a result of this encounter, a peritectoid horizontal appears at 1240°C.

Bumps, Kessler, and Hansen (5).

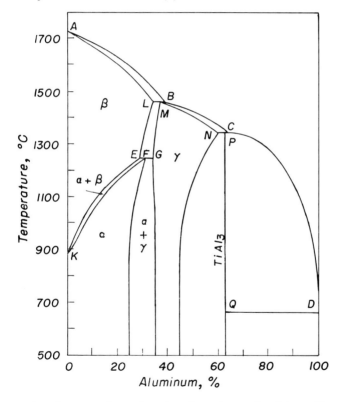

such a loop as does also the zirconium-columbium diagram. Figure 11.9 shows that the second combination of metals is complicated by the transformation in zirconium. One sees that the upper of the lines descending

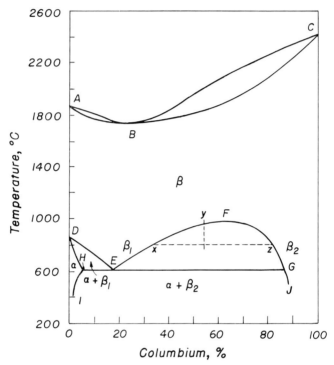

Fig. 11.9 The Monotectoid Reaction in the Zirconium-Columbium Alloy System

This system of alloys has diagram-wide solid solubility for an interval below the solidus line but at lower temperatures the solid solution decomposes into two other similar phases. Line *EFG* marks the temperature at which the decomposition starts for any composition. The intersection of this line and the line *DE* from the transformation point *D* leads to the formation of the horizontal line *HEG* that is known as a monotectoid line or monotectoid horizontal.

Rogers and Atkins *(6).*

Fig. 11.10 X-Ray Diffraction Powder Patterns of a 60% Columbium Zirconium-Columbium Alloy as Quenched From 1100°C. and From 800°C.

The upper of these diagrams shows the alloy as quenched from 1100°C. while it was in the single-phase condition. The lower strip shows the splitting of the lines when this solid solution decomposes into two other phases, in this instance, at 800°C. Rogers and Atkins (6).

from D encounters the loop at E and produces the horizontal line HEG. This arrangement of lines resembles closely the monotectic situation in Fig. 11.4. Correspondingly, it is called a "monotectoid" case.[3]

Because of the slowness with which a monotectic reaction proceeds, careful measurements may be necessary to establish its nature. One effective way is to observe the splitting of the lines in an X-ray diffraction powder pattern as depicted in Fig. 11.10. Obviously, the two solid solutions resulting from the decomposition are body-centered cubic as was the parent solid solution, β. Changes in composition and, correspondingly, of space lattice have caused the lines to shift slightly.

THE IRON-CHROMIUM DIAGRAM

One of the most interesting alloy systems involving iron is produced by the addition of chromium. Two

---

[3] Also, because of a similarity to the eutectoid arrangement, that name is used sometimes. However, in the strict sense, monotectoid appears to be the correct term in view of the similarity to the monotectic type of diagram.

features of this system, shown in Fig. 11.11, deserve attention. The lines extending from the A_3 (900°C.) and A_4 (1390°C.) transformation points ascend and descend, respectively, to meet and form a closed area usually called a "gamma loop." The second feature is the group of lines appearing at the lower center. They indicate the formation from solid solution α of a compound known as "sigma phase." This substance forms slowly and may not be detected until after hundreds or thousands of hours. However, it is brittle and must be taken into account in designs requiring iron-chromium stainless steels.

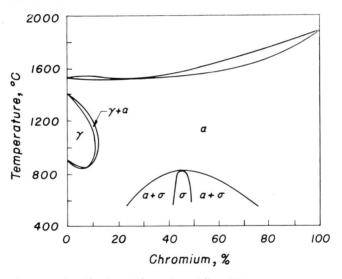

Fig. 11.11   The Iron-Chromium Alloy Diagram

In this diagram, the lines from A_4, the transformation at 1390°C., descend and those from A_3 ascend until the two sets meet. The result is an enclosed area known as a "gamma loop." Under some conditions, alloys near the center of the diagram undergo a slow conversion into a compound called sigma. This compound often reduces ductility to an undesirable degree.

REFERENCES

1. J. T. Williams: "Vanadium-Zirconium Alloy System," *Transactions,* American Institute of Mining and Metallurgical Engineers, Vol. 203, 1955, pp. 345–350.
2. "Metals Handbook," American Society for Metals, Cleveland, Ohio, 1948, p. 1200.
3. E. Pelzel: "Kupfer-Blei Legierungen 1. Das Schmelz-diagram und der Gefügeaufbau binärer Legierungen," Metall, Vol. 10, 1956, pp. 1023–1028.
4. H. K. Adenstedt, J. R. Pequignot, and J. M. Raymer: "The Titanium-Vanadium System," *Transactions,* American Society for Metals, Vol. 44, 1952, pp. 990–1003.
5. E. S. Bumps, H. D. Kessler, and M. Hansen: "Titanium-Aluminum System," *Transactions,* American Institute of Mining and Metallurgical Engineers, Vol. 194, 1952, pp. 609–614.
6. B. A. Rogers and D. F. Atkins: "Zirconium-Columbium Diagram," *Transactions,* American Institute of Mining and Metallurgical Engineers, Vol. 203, 1955, pp. 1034–1041.

Note: Diagrams for which no credit is indicated have been taken directly from the "Metals Handbook" or have been slightly modified from a diagram given in the "Metals Handbook."

CHAPTER 12

Special Arrangements of Atoms

METALS FURNISH their share of mystery stories. In a number of instances, their behavior has been unexplainable on the basis of accepted ideas. What must then be done is to imagine a mechanism that could account for the unexpected behavior and to determine whether the proposed mechanism is likely to be the correct one.

PECULIAR BEHAVIOR IN THE COPPER-GOLD ALLOYS

An unusual behavior that has been observed in a number of alloy systems was noticed first in the copper-gold alloys. Not only were the copper-gold alloys the first in which the effects were noticed but they have since been the most extensively investigated. Accordingly, this system is a suitable one on which to base a description of the phenomena.

One of the first facts noted was the increase in hardness sometimes manifested by alloys containing about 75 w/o (50 a/o) gold. Associated with this hardness was a brittleness that made fabrication difficult. The extent to which hardness may increase is evident in Fig. 12.1

Fig. 12.1   The Effect of Heat Treatment on the Hardness of a 50 a/o Gold-Copper Alloy

The alloy was quenched from a relatively high temperature so that the disordered state would be retained and then was held at 200°C. for the times indicated.
Nowack *(1)*.

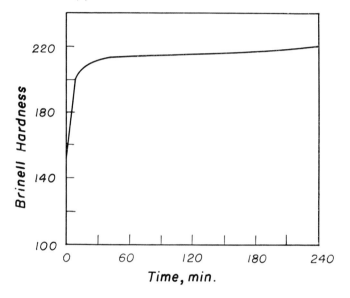

which is based on a 50 a/o copper-50 a/o gold alloy. Pieces of this alloy were first quenched from a moderately high temperature and then held for different lengths of time at 200°C. The pronounced increase in hardness during the first 30 minutes is obvious. As the alloys had solidified in a manner that indicated complete mutual solid solubility such a marked change in hardness was not anticipated. The logical expectation for such alloys is that they will change relatively little under any type of heat treatment.

THE CONSTITUTIONAL DIAGRAM OF THE COPPER-GOLD ALLOYS

Realization that the properties of the copper-gold alloys do change with heat treatment led to an investigation of their behavior and their structure at low temperature. One consequence was the introduction of the arches in the lower part of the diagram presented as

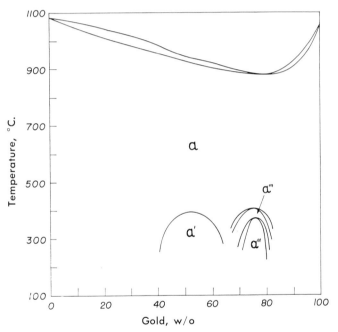

Fig. 12.2   The Constitutional Diagram of the Copper-Gold Alloys

This diagram is based on the one in the *Metals Handbook* but the arches at 75 w/o gold have been drawn in accordance with the results published by Pianelli and Faivre *(2)*. The regions designated as α″ and α‴ frequently are designated as CuAu I and CuAu II, respectively.

Fig. 12.2. Lines of this sort always signify the occurrence of some internal change.

Because the compositions in Fig. 12.2 are designated in per cent by weight, one may not notice immediately that the crests of the arches correspond to 25 a/o (per cent by atoms) gold and 50 a/o gold. These proportions suggest immediately the compounds Cu_3Au and $CuAu$ but the clue is, in the strict sense, a false one. The arches do not signify the emergence of a compound resembling the σ phase in the iron-chromium diagram of Fig. 11.11. Nor do they indicate the decomposition of a solid solution such as occurs in the zirconium-columbium alloys (Fig. 11.9). What does take place was eventually revealed by X-ray studies and was called "ordering."

ORDERING IN THE 50 ATOMIC PER CENT ALLOYS

For an interval below the solidification temperature, all copper-gold alloys are solid solutions with a face-centered cubic structure. A 50 a/o (75 w/o) gold alloy would, if magnified, resemble the model of Fig. 3.8, half of the atoms being copper and half being gold. At high temperatures, the two kinds of atoms are mixed indiscriminately. However, if the 50 a/o alloy is cooled slowly or if it is quenched and reheated to a low temperature, the atoms rearrange themselves in a special way. Based on Fig. 3.8, the rearrangement is such that the horizontal layers are composed alternately of all gold and all copper atoms. An ordered structure composed of several hundred atoms is pictured in Fig. 12.3.

Figure 12.3 may be considered as an assembly of unit cells of the ordered structure. One cell, at the upper right, near corner, is heavily outlined. Although the volume of the cells is changed relatively little by ordering, their dimensions are altered slightly. Their height decreases about 5% and their horizontal edges lengthen about 2%. The ordered cell may be described as face-centered tetragonal; the metal that it represents is described as a face-centered tetragonal metal.

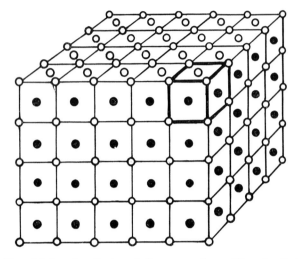

Fig. 12.3   An Ordered Structure in a 50 a/o Gold-Copper Alloy as It Exists at Room Temperature

The structure is face-centered tetragonal. A unit cell is shown at the near, upper right corner. Although not apparent from the figure, the height of the cell is slightly less than the length of the horizontal edges.

THE X-RAY POWDER PATTERN OF THE 50 a/o ALLOY

The effect of ordering in an alloy on its X-ray powder pattern is striking. Compared with the pattern of the disordered alloy, the number of lines may be approximately doubled. The two kinds of patterns are indicated by the drawing in Fig. 12.4. The one on the left represents the disordered alloy as it exists after being quenched; the one on the right represents the ordered alloy obtained when the quenched specimen is reheated to a low temperature.

The reason for these additional lines becomes evident from an examination of Fig. 12.5 which shows the reflection of X-rays from a set of planes in a crystal, or grain, of copper-gold alloy. A disordered alloy—random distribution of atoms—is shown at the upper left in this figure. Random distribution means that the proportion of each kind of atoms on a plane is about the same on every plane of a set. Therefore, the reflecting power of

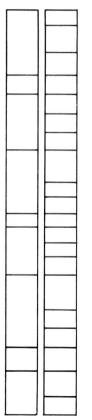

Fig. 12.4   The Effect of Ordering on the X-Ray Powder Pattern of a 50 a/o Gold-Copper Alloy

The pattern at the left was obtained from a disordered alloy; the one at the right is from an ordered alloy. Differences in intensity of lines (degree of blackening) are not indicated in the drawing.

Modified from a figure by Nix and Shockley *(3)*.

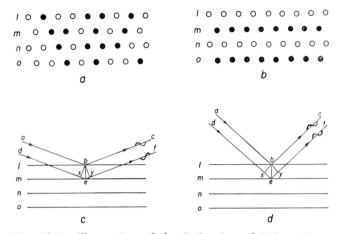

Fig. 12.5 Illustration of the Reflection of X-Rays From a Disordered and From an Ordered 50 a/o Gold-Copper Alloy.

Open circles represent copper and filled circles represent gold. Drawing a shows the disordered alloy in which the gold and the copper atoms are distributed at random with the result that each plane has about the same total weight of atoms per unit area and hence possesses the same reflecting power. In the ordered state pictured in drawing b, the copper and gold atoms gather on alternate planes. Drawing c shows the reflection of X-rays from the planes of atoms but the atoms themselves have been omitted for the sake of convenience. In c, the rays are coming in at such an angle that upon reflection, the ray from plane m is 180° (one half of a complete vibration) out of phase with respect to the ray coming from l. The reason for this situation is that the ray def has to travel farther by the distance xey, which equals one-half wave length (see Fig. 3.20). If the reflecting power of the planes is the same, the corresponding reflected rays have equal intensities and cancel each other completely. Hence, no line appears on the pattern. On the other hand, in an ordered alloy, the gold-bearing planes have much greater reflecting power than the copper-bearing planes. Consequently, the rays from the two kinds of planes do not cancel each other completely and a line does appear on the pattern.

If a line is to be formed on the pattern for the disordered crystal, the direction of the incoming rays must be changed so that the distance xey equals a full wave length as in drawing d. Of course, the ordered alloy also has a line corresponding to this direction of rays.

each of a set of parallel planes is about the same, the reflecting power being closely proportional to the weight of atoms per unit area of plane. Hence, if the rays reflected from adjacent planes, as l and m in drawing a and drawing c are 180° out of phase, they cancel each other completely and are not able to form a line on the X-ray film. A condition of this kind is depicted by the little sine waves at c and f in drawing c. As the peaks of the waves are exactly opposed, they add to zero. On the other hand, if the two planes of atoms have different weights as in an ordered alloy (drawing b) the reflected rays will be of unequal intensity—the amplitudes of the little sine waves will be unequal—and cancellation will be incomplete. Therefore, a line will appear on the pattern. Drawing d refers back to the case of the disordered alloy. It shows the direction to be given to the incoming X-rays in order that the distance xey shall equal one full wave length and, correspondingly, that the reflected rays shall be in phase.

THE SECOND FORM OF ORDERED 50 a/o ALLOY

Should the temperature of an alloy in the ordered condition described above be increased to 390°C. for a period of time, the atoms would change their positions to produce the arrangement shown in Fig. 12.6. Examination of this figure reveals that alternate planes are no longer all copper or all gold. Instead, in a horizontal direction parallel to the plane of the paper, a structural shift occurs every five atoms. Gold atoms move to planes previously occupied by copper atoms and vice-versa. The unit cell that represents this structure is equivalent to 10 tetragonal cells laid side by side. In 5 of the cells, the atoms are in different positions (lattice points) than they are in the other 5. The unit cell is 10 times as long in one horizontal direction as in the other. Such a cell is shown in the figure by a heavy outline.

The existence of two kinds of ordered 50 a/o alloy is evident in the diagram of Fig. 12.2 as the double set of

Fig. 12.6 The Arrangement of Atoms in the 50 a/o Alloy in the Temperature Range Between 375°C. and 408°C.

Over this interval of temperature, the atoms are ordered in a more complex manner than the simple ordered structure that prevails at low temperature. A shift of gold atoms to copper-bearing planes and of copper atoms to gold-bearing planes takes place at intervals of 5 atoms in one direction. The unit cell of this structure is 10 times as long as it is wide, or high.

Nix and Shockley (3).

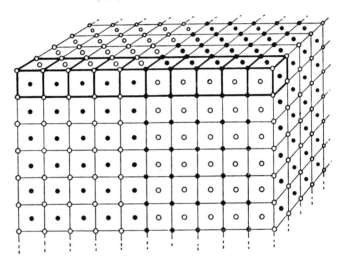

arches at 75 w/o gold. The two forms are designated as CuAu I and CuAu II. CuAu I is stable from room temperature to 375°C. whereas CuAu II exists only in the limited interval from 375°C. to 408°C. Also evident from the diagram is the existence of both forms of CuAu at compositions on either side of the 50 a/o alloy. What this situation means is that ordering still takes place even if not enough of one kind of atoms is present to fill half of the planes. For example, if a deficiency of gold atoms exists, then copper atoms, besides furnishing population for the completely copper planes, substitute for gold atoms on the gold-bearing planes. The diagram shows also that a deficiency in either kind of atom lowers the temperature at which ordering sets in.

ORDERING IN THE 25 a/o GOLD ALLOY

One might guess that the substitution of copper atoms on a gold-bearing plane or of gold atoms on a copper-bearing plane could not take place beyond some limiting degree. Accordingly, existence of a different mechanism of ordering in a 25 a/o[1] gold, or Cu_3Au alloy is not unexpected. In this alloy, gold atoms move to positions that correspond to the corners of the face-centered cubic unit cells and copper atoms move to the centers of the faces. This combination means that each unit cell has one atom of gold and 3 of copper as may be understood easily if one notes that corner atoms are shared by 8 cells and face-centered atoms by 2. As in the CuAu alloy, the rearrangement of atoms makes its presence known by the appearance of extra lines in the X-ray powder pattern. The unit cell retains its cubic character but its volume is slightly less than the volume of the cell of the disordered alloy.

CHANGE IN RESISTIVITY OF THE 25 a/o GOLD ALLOY

Ordering changes many of the properties of this alloy. One of the most prominent changes is in electrical resistivity[2] which is altered drastically, as is true also of the

---

[1] The correspondence of 50 w/o gold to 25 a/o gold and of 75 w/o gold to 50 a/o gold is purely accidental. It is the result of the relative atomic weights of gold and copper. Actually, the correspondence is only approximate.

[2] The electrical resistivity of a metal is the resistance of a cube that is one cm. on each edge. It is a characteristic of the metal, not of any particular shape.

50 a/o alloy. The manner of its change is illustrated by Fig. 12.7, curve *A*. Data for this curve were obtained on a specimen that was cooled at an extremely slow rate. One notes that when ordering begins slightly above 380°C., the initial decrease in resistance is very rapid.

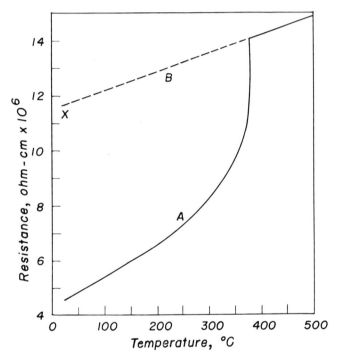

Fig. 12.7   The Abrupt Decrease in Electrical Resistance in a 25 a/o Gold-75 a/o Copper Alloy.

The decrease begins suddenly as the alloy cools through a temperature of about 380°C. Resistivity values have been multiplied by 10^6, or one million. Hence, actual values are one millionth of numbers marked along the left side.

Sykes and Evans *(4)*.

The rate diminishes gradually and below about 200°C., the curve becomes a straight line, a fact that suggests no further internal change as cooling continues. What the resistance at room temperature would have been had no ordering occurred is indicated by the point X which gives the value for the quenched specimen.

MECHANICAL CHANGES RELATED TO ORDERING IN THE 25 a/o ALLOY

Ordering does not produce in the Cu_3Au alloy the brittleness that it does in CuAu. The ordered alloy can be cold-worked without difficulty. What happens to the ordered state during cold-working is an interesting question. One might guess that mechanical deformation would disarrange the atoms, and that, at low temperature, they could not move back easily to their pre-worked, ordered positions. That this guess is a good one becomes evident from a study of Fig. 12.8. As curve A in this figure indicates, the electrical resistance of the ordered specimen increases rapidly with cold-working and when the reduction of area reaches 70%, it equals the resistance of a quenched—disordered—specimen, curve B. Apparently, this degree of deformation has disordered the alloy almost completely.

ORDERING IN OTHER ALLOYS

Ordering has been observed in a number of alloys, perhaps most commonly, those with face-centered cubic structures but also in the body-centered cubic and close-packed hexagonal types. Among the face-centered cubic, one of the most important is $FeNi_3$ in which ordering appears to be related to the high permeability magnetic alloys such as Permalloy. Among the body-centered cubic alloys, ordering produces the transition in β brass which is indicated in Fig. 5.11 by the lines in the vicinity of 450°C. β brass exhibits the striking variation in specific heat that is characteristic of such transitions. Its be-

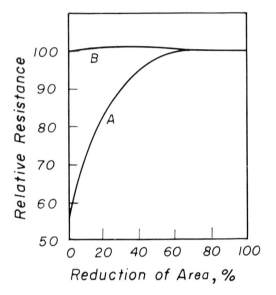

Fig. 12.8   The Effect of Cold-Working on the Electrical Resistance of an Ordered Alloy of the Composition Cu₃Au

Curve *A* shows the change in an ordered alloy and curve *B* shows the change in a disordered (previously quenched) alloy. Dahl *(5)*.

havior is illustrated in Fig. 12.9. The specific heat, that is, the heat that must be supplied to raise the temperature of one gram of alloy by 1°C., becomes relatively high when the rate of disordering reaches its maximum in the vicinity of 450°C.

ORDERING OF A DIFFERENT KIND

The ordering of alloys is complicated by a related but different behavior of atoms. In many instances, atoms

Fig. 12.9   The Sharp Increase in the Specific Heat of Brass at the Order-Disorder Transformation

The large amount of heat necessary to increase the temperature of a piece of β brass by 1°C. indicates that unusual internal changes are in progress.

Sykes and Wilkinson *(6)*.

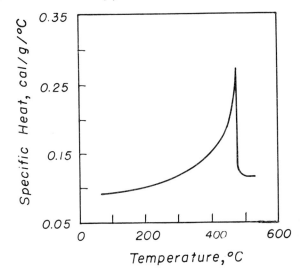

of one element such as gold, exhibit a preference for being surrounded by atoms of a different element, such as copper, rather than by atoms like themselves. Such a tendency exists in the 25 a/o gold alloy. And not only is it superposed on the ordering and disordering mechanism described previously but it persists, with rising temperature, after the alloy has become completely disordered in the sense described previously. Thus, it has the effect of delaying the attainment of complete disorder. "Short range order" is the term commonly used to describe this tendency of atoms to be surrounded by atoms unlike themselves. This name distinguishes the effect from "long range order" which has been the principal subject of this chapter. Still a different type of ordering has been suggested as a possible cause of some interesting magnetic effects. It may be described as the arrangement of like atoms in short strings with resulting anisotropic (directional) effects in the magnetism of the alloy.

Neither ordinary short range ordering nor directional ordering can be described with the exactness that is possible for long range ordering. Accordingly, no detailed analysis of the effects will be attempted but the existence of these phenomena should be noted.

REFERENCES

1. L. Nowack: "Vergütbare Edelmetall-Legierungen," *Zeitschrift für Metallkunde,* Vol. 22, 1930, pp. 94–103.
2. Antoine Pianelli and René Faivre: "Etude par diffraction des rayons X du diagramme des alliages or-cuivre de la composition equiatomic AuCu," *Comptes rendus,* Vol. 245, 1957, pp. 1537–1539.
3. Foster C. Nix and William Shockley: "Order-Disorder Transformations in Alloys," *Reviews of Modern Physics,* Vol. 10, 1938, pp. 1–71.
4. C. Sykes and H. Evans: "The Transformation in the Copper-Gold Alloy Cu₃Au," *Journal,* Institute of Metals, Vol. 58, 1936, pp. 255–280.
5. O. Dahl: "Kaltverformung und Erholung bei Legierungen mit geordneter Atomverteilung," *Zeitschrift für Metallkunde,* Vol. 28, 1936, pp. 133–138.
6. C. Sykes and H. Wilkinson: "The Transformation in the β Brasses," *Journal,* Institute of Metals, Vol. 61, 1937, pp. 223–239.

CHAPTER 13

How Metals Are Deformed

PROBABLY MOST OF US think of the deformation of metals in terms of damaged fenders or of nails that bend over when one is trying to do a bit of carpentry. However, deformation is an important step in the manufacture of fenders, nails, rails, and many other useful objects. It is the basis of an important metallurgical industry.

The behavior of metals during fabrication can be followed in a general way with the aid of a microscope. X-ray measurements on commercially made objects also have value. But more can be learned about the mechanism of deformation from laboratory studies on small pieces. Large metallic crystals have been particularly helpful in such investigations.

RELATIVE SLIP

One of the most interesting illustrations of the manner in which a crystal of metal is deformed appears in Fig. 13.1. This shows two stages in the stretching of a crystal (grain) of brass. Before stretching the crystal, the experimenters polished one side of it to a flat surface,

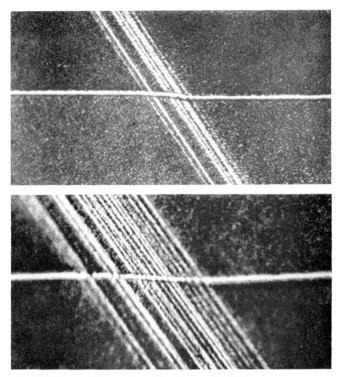

Fig. 13.1 Deformation of a Crystal of Brass

In this instance, the crystal was deformed under tension, and the horizontal line was ruled on the crystal before it was stretched. The upper figure shows the first diagonal lines that appeared as the result of stretching and also the bending of the ruled line at the point where it crosses the diagonal ones. Evidently, the right portion slipped relatively to the left. The diagonal lines, accordingly, are slip lines; that is, they are the traces of the slip planes on the polished surface. The lower figure shows how additional loading increased the number of slip lines and made a greater offset in the ruled line.

Treuting and Brick *(1)*. Magnification, 800×

and on this polished area scratched the fine straight groove that appears as the horizontal line in the photomicrographs. The first result of the tensile stress was the development of fine diagonal lines and an offset in the scratched line on the upper photomicrograph. Additional extension caused more diagonal lines to appear and also increased the offset of the horizontal line (lower figure). The obvious conclusion is that the right hand portion of the crystal slipped with respect to the left.

Relative movement of adjoining parts of a crystal has been observed in other experiments. A rod composed of only one crystal deforms, when stretched, in the manner shown in Fig. 13.2. That is, it breaks into blocks or disks which slip relatively to each other. Not apparent from the photograph is the tilting of the slabs about axes perpendicular to the axis of the specimen. This tilting is what makes possible the considerable extension of the crystal. Mainly because of it, the originally round bar becomes elliptical in cross section. Although the slipping and tilting of the disks allows a remarkable degree of extension, the individual disks change very little in shape.

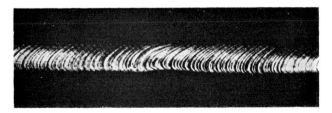

Fig. 13.2 Deformation of a Single Crystal

When subjected to a tensile load, the crystal broke into disks as the result of slip on parallel planes at more or less regular intervals. The crystal was a high-aluminum, aluminum-copper alloy. It was stretched in a tensile machine.
Elam *(2)*.

THE PLANE OF SLIP

The relative movement of disks evident in Fig. 13.2 variously called slipping, slip, or glide—takes place on parallel planes. In copper, alpha brass, aluminum, and other face-centered cubic metals, slip occurs on planes resembling the model in Fig. 13.3, known crystallographically as the (111) plane. Furthermore, the direction of slip is in one of the three directions a, b, and c.

Face-centered cubic metals have four planes like Fig. 13.3 in different positions and three directions of easy

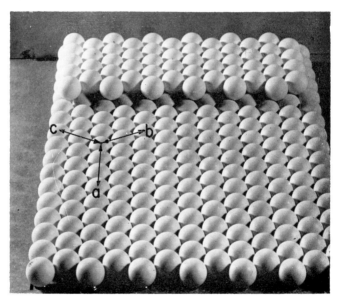

Fig. 13.3   Model of a Plane of Slip

This model represents a layer of atoms as arranged in the (111) plane of a face-centered cubic metal or the basal plane in a close-packed hexagonal metal. In these types of metals, slip always starts on a plane having this arrangement of atoms, and slip always occurs in one of the directions a, b, or c.

slip in each of the four planes. Hence, if the applied stress happens to have a suitable relationship to more than one direction of easy slip, movement may occur simultaneously on two, or possibly three planes.

THE WEAKNESS OF SINGLE CRYSTALS

Both calculations and experiments have shown that a crystal such as the one shown in Fig. 13.2 is least resistant to slip if one of its potential slip planes has a tilt

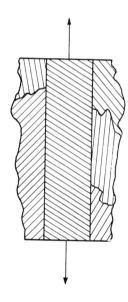

Fig. 13.4 Strengthening Effect of Surrounding Metal

This diagram depicts a single crystal of zinc with a coating of small zinc grains. In most of the surrounding grains, the slip planes will be at an angle to those in the crystal. As a consequence, the grains in the coating support the crystal so that it can break less easily into blocks that slip relatively to each other. Thus, in terms of pounds per square inch of cross section, the combination is much stronger than the single crystal alone.

of about 45° with respect to the axis. Deviation from this angle increases the stress required to initiate slipping. This fact has a connection with the greater strength of multi-grained, or "polycrystalline," metals as compared with single crystals. Obviously, if the large central grain in Fig. 13.4 were by itself, slip could take place in it under a moderate load. Also obvious is that

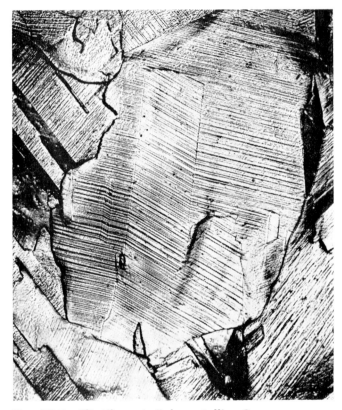

Fig. 13.5 Slip Planes in Polycrystalline Copper

This specimen was polished on one face and etched to bring out the grain boundaries. Then it was compressed in a direction parallel to the polished face until the slip lines appeared as shown. None of the adjoining grains have slip lines with the same orientation as the lines in the large central grain. Courtesy, Division of Metallurgy, National Bureau of Standards.   Magnification, 50 ×

some of the surrounding grains are less favorably oriented and would offer more resistance per unit cross-sectional area. Furthermore, those which slip with relative ease do so in such a way as to block the slipping of the central grain. The net result is that the aggregate requires a higher stress than does the single crystal if extension is to occur. That slip does take place in different directions in different grains is illustrated by the copper specimen in Fig. 13.5.

DEGREE OF SLIP AND EASE OF SLIP

So far, nothing has been said concerning any possible effect of previous slip on ease of slip. One might suppose that once slip had started and a metal crystal began breaking into blocks like the aluminum alloy bar in Fig. 13.2, it would weaken rapidly. This supposition not only is incorrect but its opposite is true. A tensile stress just sufficient to initiate slip will not cause it to continue. For slip on existing slip planes to continue or slip to begin on new planes, the tensile stress—and its component the shear stress—must be increased.

The strengthening that results from slip may be measured with some accuracy as shown in Fig. 13.6 for aluminum. In this figure, the horizontal scale indicates the extent of slip in the crystal and the vertical scale gives the force per square inch on a slip plane that will just cause slip to continue. Thus, if the slip is only 0.12, 2000 psi produces additional slip, whereas if the amount of previous slip is 0.55, a force of 4000 psi is required. Production of initial slip required only about 100 psi. Figure 13.6 represents the behavior under either tensile or compressive stresses, a fact that indicates that the stress necessary to produce slip is not influenced by another stress tending to press the blocks together or to pull them apart.

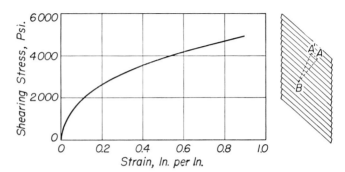

Fig. 13.6 Effect of Previous Deformation on Slip

As slipping action continues, the resistance to further slip increases. The curve shows how the force required to produce slip on 1 sq. in. of surface increases with the amount of previous slip. The extent of slip is measured by the ratio AA'/AB in the small diagram. Before slipping occurred, point A' was at position A. The graph was redrawn from G. I. Taylor *(3)*.

DEFORMATION BY TWINNING

Metals may be deformed by other processes than the slipping of one plane of atoms over another. Whole regions of atoms in a grain may shift as a unit in response to a stress. This behavior is perhaps most commonly observed in hexagonal metals (Fig. 3.11). An illustration of blocks or bands of zinc that have undergone such a shift is given in Fig. 13.7. These bands, the light-colored material in the figure, are called "mechanical twins" to distinguish them from the "annealing twins" that appear in so many annealed face-centered cubic metals and alloys. What has happened to produce the bands (twins) in Fig. 13.7 may be explained with the aid of the drawings in Fig. 13.8. Drawing A pictures a crystal, or grain, of zinc or other hexagonal metal in such a position that its base planes—those cor-

Fig. 13.7   Mechanical Twins in Zinc

The light bands in this picture of a crystal of zinc have been caused by mechanical stress. For this reason, they are called mechanical twins. The material in them has changed its orientation with respect to the surrounding, or matrix metal so that it bears the relationship shown in the following figure. This specimen was not polished and etched but is a cleavage section, that is, the photographed surface was obtained by cleaving, or splitting the crystal.
Jillson *(4)*.

responding to the horizontal planes of Fig. 3.11—lie perpendicular to the plane of the paper. In the twin, *AB,* the atoms have shifted in such a way that the planes corresponding to the base in Fig. 3.11 are no longer horizontal as in the remainder of the grain but are approximately vertical. The specific angle depends upon the particular metal in which the twin appears.

The orientation of the crystalline structure in the twin with respect to the structure of the grain can be

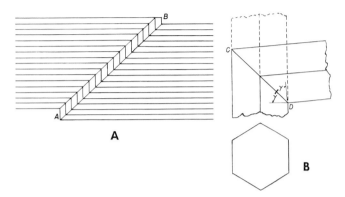

Fig. 13.8   Relative Orientation of the Crystal Structure in a Twin and in its Parent Grain

Drawing A shows a section of a crystal of a hexagonal metal of which the basal planes are perpendicular to the plane of the paper. A twin, *AB*, has developed in it. In the twinned region, the basal planes are nearly at right angles to the same planes in the parent grain.

Drawing B gives an idea of the orientation of the crystalline structure in the parent grain and in the twin. This drawing represents a structure made by piling units such as those in Fig. 3.13 on top of each other. Atoms have been omitted, however, and the structure rotated 30°. The grain represented in drawing. A has the orientation of the vertical part of the column. The twin has the orientation of the bent part. The two structures meet at the plane *CD*.

---

described with the aid of the hexagon in drawing B of Fig. 13.8. This figure has some resemblance to Fig. 3.13 but has been rotated 30° and the atoms have been omitted. It might be considered as a short section of a column of units like the one in Fig. 3.13. The grain has the orientation of the unbent portion. In the twin, the orientation corresponds to the part of the hexagon that has been bent over. Of course, in the twinning action, the atoms do not move through the distances suggested by the bending of the hexagon but rearrange themselves by very small movements into new positions that produce the same orientation.

In drawing B, the degree of bend corresponds to an axial ratio—height over edge of the base in Fig. 3.14—of about 1.63, which is the value in a model made from spheres. The axial ratio of a close-packed hexagonal metal may be less or greater than 1.63.

One fact that has been observed is that the act of twinning may take place so suddenly as to cause

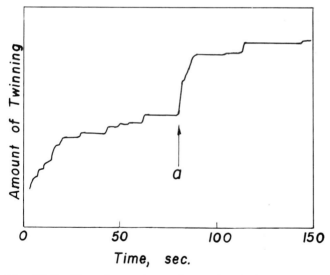

Fig. 13.9 The Formation of Mechanical Twins in Cadmium After Application of a Load

The steps indicate sudden formation of one or more twinned regions. The load was increased suddenly at *a*.
Modified from a figure by Thompson and Millard *(5)*.

a tremor of the entire piece. The intermittent nature of twin formation in a single crystal rod of cadmium is depicted in Fig. 13.9. The initial load was held constant for a time while twins continued to form and was then increased abruptly at the point indicated on the figure.

Although twinning is a prominent feature of the deformation of most close-packed hexagonal, and of some other, metals, the change of dimension of a stressed piece is mainly the result of the slipping action described in the beginning of the chapter. One effect of twinning is to move metal to such a position that the applied stress can produce slip.

TWINS IN A BODY-CENTERED CUBIC METAL

Mechanical twinning occurs also in alpha iron, a body-centered cubic metal, but ordinarily only as the result of a sharp blow. In this instance, the twins appear as narrow almost needlelike areas with irregular sides. Fig. 13.10 gives an example of such twins. Before their origin was understood, markings of this type were named "Neumann bands." As might be expected, their position is related to the arrangement of atoms; the band, or twin, always is in a direction in which the atoms lie in closely spaced strings. Planes in body-centered cubic metals are not as thickly populated with atoms as those in face-centered cubic metals.

A point of interest about these bands is that they are abundant in some pieces of old armor. However, their origin is much more likely to be the result of final hammering of the armor into shape than of combat.

DEFORMATION IN INDUSTRIAL METALS

In the interest of bringing out the details of the deformation process, most of this chapter has been devoted to what goes on in individual crystals. However, deforma-

Fig. 13.10   Mechanical Twins in Iron

These twins, often called Neumann bands, developed when the iron was deformed suddenly by a sharp blow. The direction of the twin corresponds to a direction in the grain in which atoms are very closely spaced.

Courtesy, Division of Metallurgy, National Bureau of Standards.   Magnification, 1000 ×

---

tion is important mainly because it is a factor in industrial operations. What takes place during the rolling of a brass plate or sheet becomes immediately evident from examination of Fig. 13.11 and Fig. 13.12. The first of these pictures shows brass in the fully annealed condition. The second shows how the grains have been distorted as the result of a rolling operation. Additional rolling would, of course, increase the distortion.

Fig. 13.11 Brass in the Undeformed State

The grains in this specimen are *equiaxed;* that is, the dimensions are about the same in all directions. The parallel bands appearing in most of the grains are called *twins*.
Courtesy, J. E. Burke, Institute for the Study of Metals.

Magnification, 75 ×

Degree of reduction of sheet or wire is sufficiently important to be specified quantitatively. The decrease in thickness as the result of one or several passes through a set of rolls is called the "per cent reduction." It is defined as

$$\text{per cent reduction} = \frac{\text{original thickness} - \text{final thickness}}{\text{original thickness}} \times 100$$

Because a sheet in passing through the rolls lengthens considerably but widens only a little, the per cent reduction in thickness nearly equals the per cent reduction

Fig. 13.12   Longitudinal Section of Rolled Brass Sheet

The specimen is in the *fully-hard* condition; that is, it has been reduced in thickness by 6 gage numbers, about 50%, since the previous reheating. The elongation of the grains and distortion of the *twins* is characteristic of rolled brass. Courtesy, Western Electric Co., Inc.   Magnification, 75 ×

in area of cross section. Decrease in size of wire is stated as

$$\text{per cent reduction} = \frac{\text{original area} - \text{final area}}{\text{original area}} \times 100$$

the area, of course, being the area of cross section of the

wire.   In the rolling of some metals, the practice is to make the per cent reduction per pass about the same regardless of thickness. This procedure is common with brass. As the hardness of brass increases with the degree of reduction, that is, with the number of passes through the rolls, a common way of specifying the character of the sheet is to say that it is 4 numbers hard or 6 numbers hard, meaning that it has been through either 4 or 6 passes. A sheet that is 4 numbers hard has undergone a per cent reduction of 37%. If it is 6 numbers hard, it has been reduced 50% since the last annealing (reheating) treatment.

The degree to which ductile metals can be deformed borders on the astonishing. Reductions of more than 99% are possible in copper and unalloyed iron. From the microscopic point of view, the effect of such extreme reductions is to destroy all trace of grain structure and to produce a fibrous appearance such as is apparent in the cold-rolled copper of Fig. 13.13.

Cold working, that is, deformation at or near room temperature, increases the hardness and strength of nearly all metals. This statement requires no proof to anyone who has attempted to break off a piece of wire or sheet metal by bending it back and forth a number of times. He has found that a portion once bent is less easy to bend back.

THE MECHANISM OF EXTREMELY SLOW DEFORMATION

This chapter should not be closed without mention of a special type of deformation observed in metals that are subjected to moderate loads over long periods of time, usually at slightly elevated temperatures. Such a situation exists during a "creep test" and under many industrial conditions. The applied load is insufficient to cause damage in a short-time test but is capable of producing, in hundreds or thousands of hours, a change

Fig. 13.13   Cold-Rolled   C o p p e r — Reduction 97%

Evidence of grains has been destroyed and the etched metal has assumed a fibrous appearance. The photomicrograph is placed so that the direction of rolling is vertical.

Cook and Richards (6).   Magnification, 250 ×

of dimension large enough to make the piece unusable, or, possibly, to cause rupture. What happens in a specimen subjected to tensile pull is that the piece as a whole elongates more than can be accounted for by the increase in length of the individual grains. A simple explanation is that the grains slide past each other as if their grain boundaries were an extremely viscous liquid.

Evidence for sliding along grain boundaries has been found. An example is presented in Fig. 13.14 which shows an area of surface of a specimen that had been under load at 300°C. for hundreds of hours. It has several interesting features. The scratch line that crosses the large central grain has a jog where it crosses the upper boundary of the grain. This line has a displacement at the lower boundary also but, in this in-

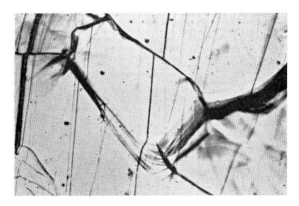

Fig. 13.14 Relative Motion (Sliding) of Grains in Aluminum Held at 300°C.

This photomicrograph shows an area of an aluminum specimen of which the surface was polished before the piece was subjected to test. The stress being relatively low, extension took place over a long time. At the right, two grains appear to have separated sufficiently to produce a pronounced gap at the boundary. In the upper center, relative movement of the two adjoining grains has caused a jog in the scratch line where it crosses the boundary. In the lower center, the boundary of the central grain appears to have moved, leaving traces of several of its positions. This movement of the boundary has caused a curvature of the scratch line.

Rachinger *(7)*.   Magnification, 250 ×

stance, the shift is gradual because of a movement of the boundary that left several traces. At the right center, two grains appear to have separated and left a chasm between them. Movements inside a piece of metal are not the same as those outside. Inside, no separations of grains are to be found. However, ways can be found to indicate that relative movements do occur inside also.

If grains of irregular shape move relatively to each other, some change in their form certainly is to be expected. Slip like that described early in this chapter would permit adjustment but little evidence of slip lines can be found in specimens like the one represented by Fig. 13.14. Possibly the slip lines heal; possibly, they are too fine to be seen under a microscope; possibly recrystallization takes place as described in the following chapter. One can hardly doubt that some internal rearrangement takes place.

REFERENCES

1. R. G. Treuting and R. M. Brick: "Micrographic Observations of Slip Lines in Alpha Brass," *Transactions, American Institute of Mining and Metallurgical Engineers,* Vol. 147, 1942, pp. 128–133.

2. Constance F. Elam: "The Distortion of Metal Crystals," Clarendon Press, Oxford, 1935.

3. G. I. Taylor: "The Distortion of Crystals of Aluminium Under Compression. Part III. — Measurements of Stress," *Proceedings,* Royal Society of London, Vol. A116, 1927, pp. 39–60.

4. D. C. Jillson: "An Experimental Survey of Deformation and Annealing Processes in Zinc," *Transactions,* American Institute of Mining and Metallurgical Engineers, Vol. 188, 1950, pp. 1009–1018.

5. N. Thompson and D. J. Millard: "Twin Formation in Cadmium," *Philosophical Magazine,* Ser. 7, Vol. 43, 1952, pp. 422–440.

6. Maurice Cook and T. Ll. Richards: "The Self-Annealing of Copper," *Journal,* The Institute of Metals, Vol. 70, 1944, pp. 159–173.
7. W. A. Rachinger: "Relative Grain Translations in the Plastic Flow of Aluminium," *Journal,* Institute of Metals, Vol. 81, 1952–53, pp. 33–41.

CHAPTER 14

Recrystallization

In a sense, recrystallization is the reverse of deformation. Although it does not reverse the slipping action and the other movements by which deformation occurred, recrystallization does return the metal approximately to its original condition. This statement holds not only for mechanical properties such as strength and ductility but also for microscopic appearance.

MEANING OF RECRYSTALLIZATION

What recrystallization means is illustrated by the series of photomicrographs of 70–30 brass displayed in Fig. 14.1. The first picture of this sequence shows the structure of the metal after it had been reduced 33% in thickness by a cold rolling operation. The grains are still recognizable but the deformation is evident from the bending of the twin bands and the numerous lines characteristic of photomicrographs of rolled brass. The next figure illustrates the effect of immersing a thin specimen of the rolled material for 3 sec. in molten lead at 580°C. Tiny new grains are beginning to appear in rows along

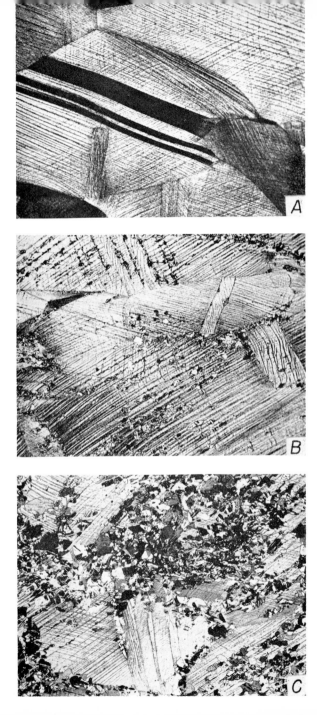

Fig. 14.1   Recrystallization of Cold-Worked Brass

This group of photomicrographs shows the process of the recrystallization of rolled brass. A shows the alloy after the rolling operation, in which the reduction was 33%. The numerous lines, characteristic of rolled brass, probably are traces of
slip planes over which movement took place during rolling.
B shows the new grains beginning to form in the slip lines
particularly where they are intersected by cross lines or bands.
C to E show successive stages in the development and growth
of the new grains. The specimens were heated at 580°C. in a
lead bath for the following periods: B, 3 sec.; C, 4 sec.; D, 8
sec.; E, 1 hr.

Courtesy, J. E. Burke, Institute for the Study of Metals.

Magnification, 75 ×

the lines which probably are traces of slip planes. They are most abundant where the traces encounter cross lines or bands. The development of more new grains is apparent in Fig. 14.1C, which is a micrograph of metal that has been heated at 580°C. for 4 sec. Figure 14.1D indicates that 8 sec. at 580°C. suffices to eliminate almost all traces of the former grain structure and to convert the metal into an aggregate of new grains. The recrystallizing process appears to be complete at this point and some growth of new grains has occurred. In Fig. 14.1E, considerable additional growth is evident. Figure 13.11 actually is the last picture in this series and could be considered to be Fig. 14.1F.

GROWTH OF GRAINS

Obviously, growth of grains is a different process from recrystallization. In recrystallization, new grains develop in the deformed metal as tiny nuclei, and grow by the acquisition of atoms that leave the deformed regions to take up a new alignment in the recrystallized grains. Grain growth takes place in metals that have been converted already to new, and presumably unstrained grains; consequently, it can occur only if some grains devour other grains. Also, it reduces the number of grains in any volume.

A reduction in the number of grains in a volume means a decrease in the total area of grain boundaries in that volume. Also, according to the theory of surface or interface energy, a decrease in interface area corresponds to a decrease in total surface energy in the volume. Since changes tend to occur in the direction that reduces energy, grain growth is to be anticipated if the temperature rises to a value that gives mobility to the atoms. Such a theory gives very little notion of the mechanism by which an atom of a grain being devoured detaches itself from its associates and crosses a grain boundary to attach itself to a growing grain. Unfortunately, for the present, we are unable to picture the details of these movements.

CONDITIONS FOR RECRYSTALLIZATION

The general conditions for the recrystallization of a cold deformed metal or alloy are fairly well known. The temperature at which a piece is maintained, the length of time during which the piece is at the temperature, and the nature of the deformation are all important, but the fundamental factor is the character of the material itself. Tungsten that has been deformed cold can be heated to about 900°C. without showing any evidence of recrystallization. On the other hand, lead and some other soft metals recrystallize at room temperature or below.

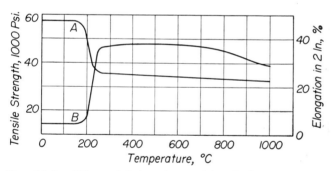

Fig. 14.2   Effect of Reheating Cold-Rolled Copper

The sheet material used in these tests had been rolled through 10 Browne & Sharpe gage numbers, a cold reduction of about 70%, without reheating. Specimens cut from it were heated for half-hour periods at different temperatures. A sharp decrease in strength and increase in percentage of elongation took place in the range from 175°C. to 250°C. Since the percentage of elongation measured in a tensile test is a rough indication of the ductility of the metal, a marked increase in ductility evidently accompanies the decrease in tensile strength. This graph was redrawn from Bassett and Davis (1).

Fig. 14.3 Copper Recrystallizing at Room Temperature

These photomicrographs show the metal of Fig. 13.13 (cold rolled to 97.5% reduction) as it appeared 4 and 16 weeks, respectively, after being rolled. The white areas indicate recrystallized regions. The action is well started after 4 weeks and nearly half of the specimen is converted in 16 weeks. Very little, dark, unconverted metal remained after one year. Cook and Richards (2). Magnification, 250×
A—After 4 Weeks. B—After 16 Weeks.

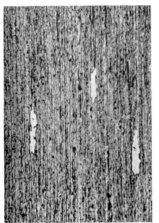 

Usually, a statement on the temperature of recrystallization of a metal is based on practical time intervals—that is, periods of 15 min. to several hours. For example, in Fig. 14.2, which shows the effect of recrystallization on the tensile strength and percentage elongation of specimens of copper, the heating periods were ½ hr. long.[1]

TEMPERATURE FACTOR

According to Fig. 14.2, a temperature in excess of 200°C. is necessary to bring about recrystallization in ½ hr.

[1] The initial changes may occur before recrystallization begins. See the section on Recovery later in this chapter.

However, if sufficient time is allowed and if other conditions are favorable, severely cold-worked copper recrystallizes at room temperature. This fact is illustrated in Fig. 14.3 which shows a piece of the same copper that was exhibited in Fig. 13.13 after being at 27°C. for periods of 4 weeks and 16 weeks respectively. After 4 weeks, recrystallization becomes evident as shown by the first of these figures, and after 16 weeks, nearly half of the specimen is converted. Recrystallization of this piece approached completion after about one year.

Recrystallization is speeded up greatly if the temperature is increased. For example, at 125°C. specimens of the copper described in the previous paragraph began to recrystallize in a few minutes and were completely converted in ½ hr.

The apparent discrepancy between a recrystallization temperature of 125°C. and one of about 225°C., as indicated in Fig. 14.2, seems to call for a little explanation, especially since the heating times were approximately ½ hr. in each instance. Part of this difference, perhaps a large part of it, is to be ascribed to the greater degree of reduction, 97.5%, of the 125°C. material as compared with the milder reduction of only 70% for the copper of Fig. 14.2. An increase in the amount of cold work does lower the temperature of recrystallization.

PRIOR GRAIN SIZE

A factor not mentioned yet but certainly important in fixing the recrystallization temperature of a metal is the size of the grains before the deformation takes place. For example, in the same group of tests that supplied the material for Fig. 14.3, there were other specimens which did not begin to recrystallize (at 27°C.) until nearly three years after they were rolled. Yet, they differed from the specimens of the photomicrographs only in having a grain size of about 0.06 mm. instead of 0.025 mm. before being cold worked.

ALLOYING AFFECTS RECRYSTALLIZATION

Recrystallization temperatures of the so-called unalloyed metals may be influenced strongly by fractional percentages of other elements. Sometimes this effect is desirable. For example, copper tubes and sheet used for automobile radiators are strengthened by the cold working they receive during fabrication but they lose this strength if they recrystallize from the heat of a soldering operation. However, if the copper contains a few hundredths of a per cent of silver, or, perhaps contains a little of some other suitable element, the recrystallization temperature is sufficiently high that no difficulty from soldering operations will occur.

The temperature of recrystallization of aluminum changes rapidly with the content of alien elements. A good grade of industrial aluminum may soften at 200°C., or a little above, but specially purified metal may recrystallize at 100°C. Composition undoubtedly was a factor in the difference in the softening behaviors of the different kinds of copper described in this chapter.

THE DEGREE OF DEFORMATION

Not only does the degree of the deformation influence the temperature of recrystallization but it has a considerable effect on the size of the grains that form during any recrystallizing treatment. For a specific metal and a definite temperature of reheating, the pertinent facts may be represented by a graph like the one shown in Fig. 14.4 for steel bars about ½ in. thick, heated 3 hr. at 850°C. One notes especially three features of this graph:

1. For recrystallization to occur at all, the deformation must exceed a minimum value. In the graph, the minimum value corresponded to a decrease of about 6.5% in the height of the rolled bar.

2. The recrystallized grains have maximum size if the deformation exceeds the minimum value only slightly.

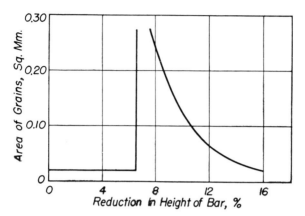

Fig. 14.4   How Deformation Affects Size of New Grains

This diagram illustrates for low-carbon iron, the relationship between degree of deformation and size of grains in the reheated metal. It is for specimens taken after the cold-rolled bars had been heated for 3 hr. at 850°C. No recrystallizing action takes place unless the reduction in thickness exceeds a minimum value of about 6.5%. If the deformation exceeds this minimum amount only slightly, the grains that develop as the result of heating are very large. However, for still greater deformation, the recrystallized grains are smaller as indicated. The behavior depicted by this figure is characteristic of metals but the proportions of the diagram change considerably according to the metal or alloy. This graph was redrawn from Kaiser and Taylor *(3)*.

3. In the higher degrees of deformation, the size of the recrystallized grains decreases as the degree of deformation increases.

Figure 14.5 is an illustration of the second statement. It shows large grains developing in a specimen of 1% silicon (electrical) steel that was elongated 4% in tension—about the minimum deformation necessary for recrystallization—and then reheated. Before the piece was

Fig. 14.5 Large Grains in Silicon Steel

If silicon steel (iron-silicon alloy) is deformed slightly in excess of the minimum for recrystallization, it may develop very large grains upon being reheated. This specimen contained 1% silicon. It was elongated 4% and then heated at 800°C. for 30 min. Such large grains indicate that the deformation exceeded only slightly the minimum necessary for recrystallizing action. The mottled background shows the grain size as it was before the piece was deformed and heated.

Courtesy, James K. Stanley, Westinghouse Research Laboratory.   Magnification, 5 ×

stretched, its etched cross section resembled the mottled background in the micrograph. Reheating for 30 min. at 800°C. after stretching caused the development and growth of the large rounded grains. A longer period of heating would have caused these grains to grow and new grains to develop and grow until the entire surface was covered with very large grains. By careful control of the degree of deformation and of the time and temperature of the subsequent heating operation, one may produce very large grains of metal; in fact, so large that one grain may constitute an entire specimen. The aluminum-copper crystal used in the experiment of Fig. 13.2 had been made in this way. Iron and aluminum are particularly disposed to the growth of large grains.

The third of the above statements relates to the right portion of Fig. 14.4. It may be illustrated by a tapered test piece. When such a piece is extended in tension, the small end will be loaded to a higher stress than the large one and will undergo greater deformation. According to Fig. 14.4, the grains in the reheated piece should be smallest at the small end. The correctness of this prediction is confirmed by the aluminum specimen in Fig. 14.6.

Figure 14.7 is introduced because it emphasizes comments made previously in this chapter. It shows a piece of copper, originally a single crystal, that has been deformed by rolling and then reheated to cause partial recrystallization. The still deformed metal in the lower portion of the photomicrograph is separated from the recrystallized grain in the upper by the stepped line. Apparently, the new grain is growing downward and devouring the deformed region. One sees that the pattern of fine lines visible in the deformed area is absent in the recrystallized grain. On the other hand, the light-colored recrystallized portion shows dark-colored bands that are the twins so often observed in face-centered cubic metals that have been deformed and recrystallized.

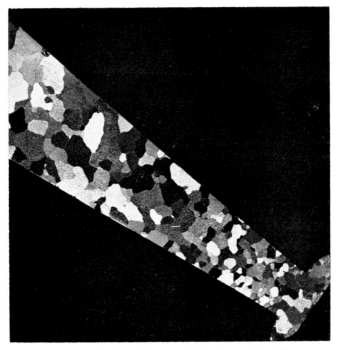

Fig. 14.6 Grains in a Tapered Aluminum Test Piece

When this piece was loaded in tension the small end was stressed more heavily than the large one and experienced a greater deformation. In accordance with Fig. 14.4, the grains formed as the result of subsequent heating are smallest at the small end.

Courtesy, J. E. Burke, Institute for the Study of Metals.

¾ Actual Size

RECRYSTALLIZATION SOFTENS

The softening effect of recrystallization is evident in Fig. 14.7 from the larger indentations made in the upper area by the hardness tester. One notes that the indentation in

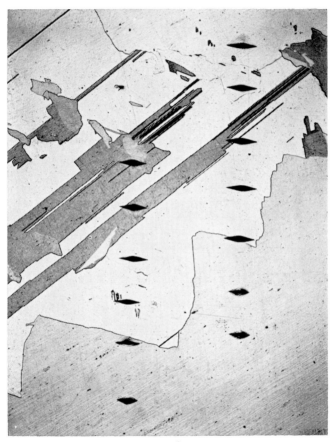

Fig. 14.7　Recrystallization of Copper

This specimen, originally a single crystal, was deformed by rolling and then heated to a low temperature for a short time. The still deformed metal in the lower part of the photomicrograph is separated from the recrystallized grain in the upper area by the stepped line. Diamond-shaped indentations made by the Knoop hardness tester are larger on the soft metal.

Courtesy, Division of Metallurgy, National Bureau of Standards.　　　　　　　　　　　　　　　Magnification, 50 ×

the left column immediately below the stepped boundary is slightly larger than others in the area of deformed metal. One can not be sure whether the larger indentation is caused by the presence of recrystallized metal immediately below the surface or whether a slight softening actually occurs in advance of recrystallization.

PREFERRED ORIENTATION

Recrystallization does not always return a metal to its predeformed condition in one respect. The metal may differ in the way its grains lie in the piece. If the cold-rolling of a piece of copper is not continued beyond about 50% reduction, subsequent heating will return the piece essentially to its prerolled condition of randomly oriented grains. On the other hand, if the rolling is continued until the reduction is 95% or more, the grains in the recrystallized metal will not be oriented in the random manner that existed before rolling. Instead, they will all have a common relationship to the direction of rolling that is described as "preferred orientation." The piece itself is stated to have a "texture." Recrystallization of a heavily cold-rolled sheet produces a preferred orientation like that in Fig. 14.8. As this figure indicates, the new grains are oriented in such a way that their unit cells have faces parallel (and perpendicular) to the surface of the sheet. Also, the sides of cells are related to the direction of rolling as shown by the figure. In crystallographic language, the orientation is stated as (100) [001], meaning that a (100)-type plane is parallel to the surface of the sheet and a [001]-type direction is parallel to the direction in which the sheet went through the rolls, i.e., the "direction of rolling." A texture of this type is called a "cube texture." Of course, not all of the grains are in exactly the same position; there is some scatter.

Obviously, if no orientation exists in a piece that was reduced not more than 50% before it was annealed and

Fig. 14.8 The Orientation of Grains in Cold-Rolled and Annealed Copper

The copper sheet, or strip, underwent heavy reduction by cold rolling and was then heated to produce recrystallization. All of the grains have approximately the same orientation with respect to the sheet. Their positions can be represented by the cubic unit cell sitting with one face on the sheet and two of its other faces parallel to the direction of rolling (the direction in which the sheet went through the rolls).

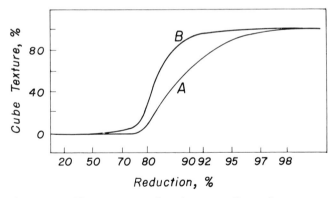

Fig. 14.9 How Degree of Reduction Affects the Texture of Rolled and Annealed Strip

These curves represent the condition of copper strip after an annealing treatment following the amounts of reduction indicated. Curve A is for strip annealed at 400°C. and curve B represents the strip after heating at 983°C.
Baldwin (5).

almost complete orientation is present in a piece that was reduced 95% or more before reheating, some change must occur between these two degrees of deformation. How cold work affects the proportion of a sheet that becomes oriented—takes a texture—during subsequent annealing is shown in Fig. 14.9. This figure indicates, also, that the degree of cold working necessary to produce the texture pictured in Fig. 14.8 during a subsequent reheating depends to some extent on the temperature during that treatment. As to the conditions in the portions of the sheet that do not have the cube texture, the situation is less clear. One suggestion is that these regions still retain the texture they had before they were heated.

THE TEXTURE OF COLD-ROLLED COPPER

The previous section contains the assumption that the rolled sheet had a texture of some kind before it was recrystallized by the annealing treatment. This assumption is well founded. In the example of the sheet reduced 95% or more in thickness by rolling, the previously randomly oriented grains undergo extreme deformation into a mass of material of which the greater part is oriented as indicated by Fig. 14.10. The equivalent crystallographic description is (123) [1$\bar{2}$1]. When so-oriented material recrystallizes, it is converted mainly to the (100) [001] texture.

Severe deformation of any kind produces a texture and different kinds of deformation produce different textures in the same metal. Furthermore, the same kind of deformation may produce different textures in different metals.

CHANGES WITHOUT RECRYSTALLIZATION—RECOVERY

A severely deformed metal undergoes minor changes in properties even before evidence of recrystallization can be detected. This behavior is not astonishing because

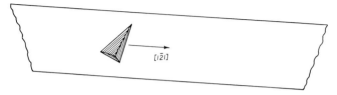

Fig. 14.10   Position of the Unit Cells in Copper After Severe Reduction by Cold Rolling

This figure shows a corner of a cube lying on a sheet of heavily reduced copper. All of the cube beyond the (123) plane has been removed. This (123) section coincides with the surface of the sheet. The [121] direction in the cube lies in the (123) plane. Hence, it lies also in the surface of the rolled sheet. In this instance it is parallel to the direction of rolling.

---

the deformation has introduced energy into the metal in excess of the amount it contained in the annealed condition. Therefore, the metal will tend to return to its normal state if suitable conditions are established. An increase in temperature not sufficient to produce recrystallization may increase the mobility of the atoms sufficiently for some return to take place. This tendency to return toward the undeformed condition is called "recovery."

Several changes take place during recovery. One of the most evident occurs in X-ray patterns. Deformation causes the lines in the X-ray powder pattern of a metal (see Fig. 3.3) to become broadened and less sharp in outline. Heating of the specimen to a point still below the temperature of recrystallization causes these lines to become narrower and sharper. Under the same treatment, electrical resistivity, which is increased by cold working, returns in some degree toward its value for the undeformed state. Although often not evident at as low reheating temperatures as the X-ray effect and the change of resistivity, mechanical properties move toward the values they had in the undeformed condition.

The mechanical aspects of recovery are of particular interest. One effect is the improved ductility in deformed metals, particularly in low-carbon steels. An industrial aspect is the low temperature heat treatment of steels that is called "stress relief." Another practice related to recovery is the low temperature annealing of brass to eliminate "season cracking."

THE FORMATION OF SUBGRAINS

An effect that seems not to be describable exactly as either recovery or recrystallization is the formation of "subgrains." Markings suggestive of subgrains have been observed for many years. Originally, they were called "veining." In recent years, the nature of subgrains has been studied in some detail. As the name implies, they are portions of a common grain that has lost its homogeneity and disintegrated into smaller units each of which has nearly but not exactly the same crystallographic orientation as the parent grain possessed. They are formed after moderate deformation and a reheating to low temperature.

One explanation of the formation of subgrains is based on the following simplified analysis. Suppose that a single crystal of metal has been bent and that the slip planes have curved slightly as shown in drawing a of Fig. 14.11. The curvature of both the upper and lower surfaces of the slabs must be the same but the upper surface must be a bit longer. Hence, one must expect that on the upper side of each slab an occasional separation of planes of atoms will take place and that these separations will produce tiny gaps or crevices[2] as shown in

---

[2] According to the theories in Chapter 15, these gaps would be called "dislocations."

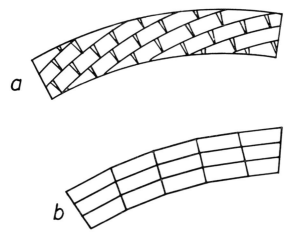

Fig. 14.11   A Hypothetical Process for Forming Subgrains

This figure illustrates one way in which subgrains might be formed. It depicts a crystal that has been bent slightly with the result that its slip planes have become curved laminae. Because the curvature of the top and bottom surfaces of any slab must be the same, the top surface must be extended relatively. Hence, the planes of atoms that are nearly perpendicular to these laminae have a tendency to separate so that gaps are produced. If the bent crystal is heated moderately, the gaps tend to line up so that small individual grains form in the crystal. These are called "subgrains." During the heating, the laminae tend to flatten.

This description has been modified and simplified from one given by Hibbard and Dunn (6).

---

drawing a. Reheating the crystal to a low temperature causes these gaps to line up and form boundaries as depicted in drawing b. At the same time, the slip planes flatten in the manner indicated in the drawing. The sections between the boundaries are called subgrains. The crystal is described as having undergone "polygonization."

REFERENCES

1. W. H. Bassett and C. H. Davis: "Physical Characteristics of Commercial Copper-Zinc Alloys," *Transactions,* American Institute of Mining and Metallurgical Engineers, Vol. 78, 1928, pp. 55–71.
2. Maurice Cook and T. Ll. Richards: "The Self-Annealing of Copper," *Journal,* Institute of Metals, Vol. 70, 1944, pp. 159–173.
3. Herman F. Kaiser and Howard F. Taylor: "The Effect of Type of Cold Deformation on the Recrystallization Properties of Armco Iron," *Transactions,* American Society for Metals, Vol. 27, 1939, pp. 227–263.
4. James K. Stanley: "Effect of Variables on the Recrystallization of Silicon Ferrite in Terms of Rates of Nucleation and Growth," *Transactions,* American Institute of Mining and Metallurgical Engineers, Vol. 162, 1945, pp. 116–138.
5. William M. Baldwin, Jr.: "Effect of Rolling Upon the Crystallography, Metallography, and Physical Properties of Copper Strip," *Transactions,* American Institute of Mining and Metallurgical Engineers, Vol. 166, 1946, pp. 591–611.
6. W. R. Hibbard, Jr. and C. G. Dunn: "Polygonization," a chapter in "Creep and Recovery," American Society for Metals, Cleveland, 1957.

CHAPTER 15

Some New Concepts Concerning Metals

MENTION WAS MADE in Chapter 7 of the possibility that vacant atom sites exist in metals, that is, that some positions at which atoms might be expected to be found actually are unoccupied. In a sense, the introduction of this concept was an act of desperation. All other imagined mechanisms had failed to provide a satisfactory explanation for the diffusion of atoms in metals.

IDEAS ABOUT VACANT ATOM SITES

The theory that was developed from the hypothesis of vacant atom sites assumes that for a particular temperature an equilibrium number of such sites exists. The equilibrium number increases with temperature. A consequence of this idea is that if vacancies can be held in place during a quenching operation as metal atoms often can, a quenched specimen should contain more than an equilibrium number of vacant sites, or vacancies.

Excess vacancies might be expected to increase the total volume beyond the dimensions that would be expected from calculations based on the average distance between atoms as determined by X-rays. Also to be expected is an increase in electrical resistivity—or decrease in conductivity—as compared with the normal value. Lack of a metal atom undoubtedly would decrease the conductivity of the small region containing the vacancy.

EVIDENCE FOR THE EXISTENCE OF VACANCIES

Although proof of the existence of vacancies might seem hard to find, some fairly substantial evidence has been obtained. One bit has already been described. In Chapter 7, a description was given of the porosity that developed in a piece of brass that had undergone a net loss of atoms by diffusive action. The net outward movement left vacant sites that gradually agglomerated into multiple vacancies. These eventually became large enough to be visible under a microscope.

A test of the idea, suggested in the previous section, that vacancies might account for some of the increase in volume as a metal is heated has been made on aluminum and on silver. Rods of these elements were found to increase more rapidly in length than could be accounted for by the spreading apart of their atoms as determined by X-rays. How the two rates compare in an aluminum rod is illustrated in Fig. 15.1. The simplest explanation of the divergence of the curves for measured length and for interatomic distance is a relatively rapid formation of vacant sites.

Resistance changes are also in accord with the idea of vacancies. For example, an increase in the number of vacancies appears to explain why the resistance of gold wires is higher as the temperature from which they are quenched is raised. An illustration of this effect is given in Fig. 15.2. In these experiments, the wires were quenched into water at room temperature but the measurements were made with the specimen

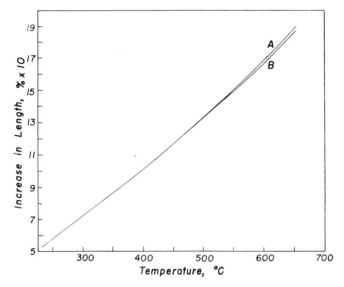

Fig. 15.1   The Increase With Rising Temperature of the Length and Interatomic Spacing of an Aluminum Rod

The figure shows that the length of the rod, curve *A*, increases more rapidly than does the interatomic distance, or lattice parameter, curve *B*.
Simmons and Balluffi *(1)*.

at the temperature of liquid nitrogen, —195°C. Small differences in resistance are accentuated if the measurements are made at low temperature. Gold has the advantage in such tests that it does not react with oxygen or nitrogen when heated.

THE DIFFUSION OF QUENCHED-IN VACANCIES

Vacancies are imagined to diffuse much as atoms do. What probably happens is that an adjacent atom drops into a vacant site leaving its former position unoccupied.

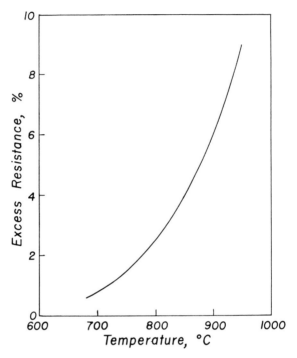

Fig. 15.2 Effect of Temperature of Quenching Upon the Cold Resistance of Gold Wires

The specimens were quenched in water at ordinary temperature but resistance measurements were made at −195°C. (78° abs.).

Graph was drawn from data in Bauerle, Klabunde, and Koehler *(2)*.

However, one speaks of the vacancy as migrating or diffusing. If the quenched gold wires of the previous section are held at room temperature, the excess resistance diminishes with time. The logical explanation of this behavior is that the vacancies held in place by quenching move slowly to the surface of the wire, to grain boundaries, to dislocations (see latter part of this chapter) or to some other irregularity in the crystalline structure. The result is that the number of vacancies left in the regular portion of the crystal approaches the equilibrium number for room temperature. An example of the decrease in resistance with time is given in Fig. 15.3. An interesting point is that the length of the

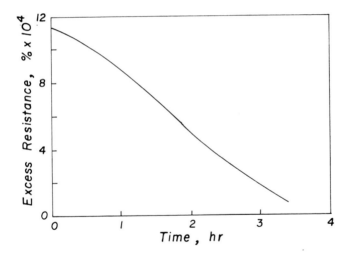

Fig. 15.3   The Decrease of Excess Electrical Resistance With Time

Gold wires were quenched in water and then held at room temperature for the times indicated on the graph. Measurements of resistance were made at 4° Kelvin (absolute). Reduction of resistance indicates reduction in the number of vacancies.

Bauerle and Koehler *(3)*.

specimen changes in about the same proportion as the resistance, a fact that suggests that vacancies are responsible for both effects.

DEFORMATION MAKES DIFFUSION OF VACANCIES EASIER

Experiments have shown that if a metal is subjected to deformation soon after it has been quenched, the rate at which the excess resistance diminishes is greatly increased. The explanation usually given of this rapid decrease is that the excess vacancies have more places to which they can diffuse. Deformation is believed to cause a sharp increase in the number of dislocations and other defects that can act as sinks for catching the diffusing vacancies. Thus, the vacancies do not have so far to travel as in a merely quenched specimen and are able to vanish more quickly.

A PECULIAR DEFECT IN METALS

Physicists who studied metals were puzzled by the discrepancies between measured values of strength and the values calculated from interatomic attractions. For example, the calculated tensile strengths usually are many times as high as those determined in a tensile testing machine. An attempt to account for this difference led to the idea of a kind of crystalline irregularity that has been named a "dislocation." Considerable interest has developed in dislocations because they can serve as a basis for a mechanism that explains in a qualitative way why metals do not have the calculated strength.

A SIMPLE DISLOCATION

Ideas about the nature of dislocations have multiplied rapidly in recent years. Early concepts of a dislocation might be represented in a general way as pictured in Fig. 15.4. This drawing, more detailed than the usual

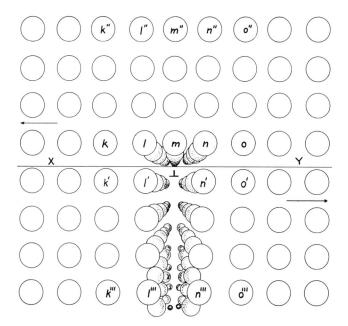

Fig. 15.4 Flaw in a Crystal Caused by the Absence of Part of a Plane of Atoms

This figure shows a region of a crystal in the vicinity of the missing partial plane. XY is the trace of a slip plane that is perpendicular to the plane of the paper. Shearing forces directed as shown will cause the upper portion of the crystal to move to the left, relative to the lower portion. This slipping action is imagined to take place by a simple mechanism in which planes in the lower left portion move successively to the right. First, plane l''' l' would move to fill the gap, that is, atom l' would come under atom m. Then the next plane, k''' k' would shift so that atom k' lay under l and so on. Continuation of this process would bring the gap to the left side of the crystal which would then show an offset as depicted in Fig. 15.5.

illustration, shows a cross section of a hypothetical metallic crystal with a primitive cubic unit cell (neither body-centered nor face-centered). The upper part contains an extra plane as compared with the lower. Correspondingly, a gap exists in the lower part. The failure of the planes in the two parts to match gives rise to a dislocation.

Dislocations are of interest mainly because they are able to move. As Fig. 15.4 indicates, the movement of the dislocation is related to a slip plane similar to those described in Chapter 13. In the figure, the slip plane is depicted as being horizontal, that is, perpendicular to the plane of the paper. Its trace is marked *XY*. The association of a slip plane with a dislocation is to be expected as slip is most likely to occur where the crystalline structure is weak and a dislocation is a region of weakness. How movement of the dislocation takes place and to what distance from the slip plane the atoms are disturbed can only be guessed at. On the assumption that the forces are directed as shown in Fig. 15.4, the lower part of the crystal must move to the right relatively to the portion above the slip plane. Or, equivalently, the upper part moves to the left. One can imagine that initial movement occurs by the plane of atoms *l''' l'* moving to the right to fill the gap. Atom *l'* would then lie under *m*. This motion would produce a new gap located under *l,* or one might say that the dislocation had moved to the left by one atom distance. This movement of planes could be repeated until the dislocation reached the left edge of the crystal. A result would be that the upper part of the crystal had an overhang one plane of atoms thick with respect to the lower portion. The entire crystal would show offsets as depicted in Fig. 15.5. What the presence of this dislocation has accomplished is to make the slipping action much easier than if the entire upper portion had to be pushed as a unit over the lower part by one atom distance.

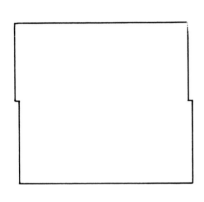

Fig. 15.5 Cross Section of a Crystal Through Which an Edge Dislocation Has Passed

The dislocation was a p o s i t i v e dislocation (extra plane above the slip plane) and passed through the crystal from right to left. The result of the passage was the formation of the steps, or offsets at the sides of the crystal. The offsets have a width of one interatomic distance.

The simple mechanical picture of planes of atoms moving en masse into gaps as described in the previous paragraph is useful for bringing out the elements of a dislocation. It gives no consideration to the forces operating between atoms. It is these forces that hold the crystal together and make it mechanically strong. One may imagine the planes of atoms immediately above and below the slip plane XY to be representable by a drawing such as Fig. 15.6. As before, the extra plane of atoms is assumed to lie in the portion of the crystal above the slip plane. Atoms above XY presumably are in some degree of lateral compression; those below it in some degree of tension. Application of forces like those shown in Fig. 15.4 probably would have only a minor effect on the interatomic spacing in the upper part of the crystal but would produce a greater effect on the spacing below. A detailed analysis of the situation in Fig. 15.6 is not simple but the possibility exists that some action, perhaps mechanical strain plus thermal agitation would cause l' to jump under atom m. The effect would be to move the dis-

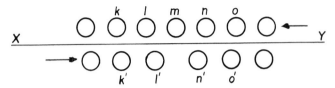

Fig. 15.6   A Dislocation Imagined as Based on Inter-atomic Forces

The planes of atoms immediately above and immediately below the slip plane are assumed to be the ones of major importance. Presumably, atoms above the slip plane are under compression and those below under tension. One can imagine that the tendency of the shearing stresses to move l' toward m plus thermal agitation could make the attraction between l' and m greater than that between l' and l. The consequence would be the movement of l' to the right.

location one atom spacing to the left. As in the mechanical picture, this process could continue to the face of the crystal.

EDGE DISLOCATIONS—THE DISLOCATION LINE

The dislocation pictured in Fig. 15.4 may be described in a more definite way. In particular, its position may be specified by a "dislocation line" that, in this instance, is a line lying in the slip plane XY, perpendicular to the paper and immediately below the extra plane of atoms mm''. In the figure, this dislocation line is marked by an inverted T. The line has the additional property that it separates the part of the crystal in which the atoms have been disturbed from the part in which they have not. Because the extra plane of atoms mm'' has an exposed edge where it terminates above the gap, this type of dislocation is called an "edge" dislocation. If the extra plane lies in the upper portion of the crystal, the dislocation is considered to be "positive"; if it lies in the lower portion, the dislocation is described as "negative."

SCREW DISLOCATIONS

A second type of dislocation is produced if one exerts a shearing stress on a crystal in the manner illustrated by the next three figures. In these figures, no atoms are shown but they would lie at the intersections of the lines if present. Figure 15.7 shows the crystal in the undeformed state. Figure 15.8 depicts its condition after

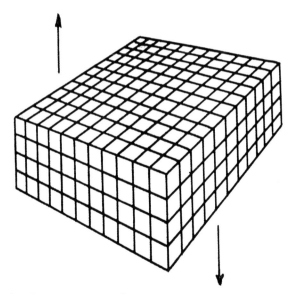

Fig. 15.7 A Hypothetical Crystal Containing No Dislocations

The crystal is imagined to have a primitive cubic unit cell and to undergo slip on a (100) type plane. According to this sketch, the stresses have not yet produced any deformation of the crystal.

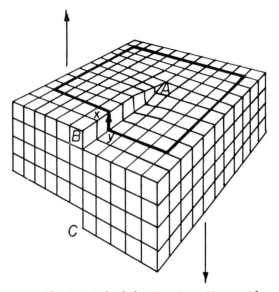

Fig. 15.8   The Crystal of the Previous Figure After Slip Action Has Started

Slip started at the front of the crystal and has progressed toward the back as far as line *AD* (*D* is directly below *A*) which is the dislocation line. In this instance, the dislocation is of the screw type. It is called a screw dislocation because a spiral path can be traced from the bottom plane to the top one if the path encloses the dislocation line.

---

slipping action has set in and has extended as far as line *AD*. (*D* lies directly below *A*.) *AD* is the dislocation line. It is the boundary between the slipped and unslipped portions of the crystal. One notes that in the "screw dislocation," the dislocation line is parallel to the direction in which the shearing forces are applied whereas, in the edge dislocation, it was perpendicular to them. In Fig. 15.9, the dislocation line has passed

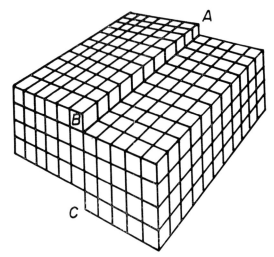

Fig. 15.9   The Crystal of the Previous Figures After the Slip Had Progressed Completely Across It

The dislocation line is imagined to have passed out of the crystal at the rear.

---

entirely out of the crystal leaving the offset condition shown. Why a dislocation of the type just described should be called a screw dislocation becomes evident if one observes that a line beginning on the top plane of Fig. 15.8 can follow an uninterrupted spiral path to the bottom plane. The first turn of the spiral is marked by a heavy line. Obviously, the same path can be followed in the reverse direction.

A few matters of terminology should be brought up at this point. First is the matter of the "slip vector." This vector defines unit slip distance in the direction in which slip occurs. In Fig. 15.8, it is indicated by the vercal arrow *yx* marked on the slip plane. In this figure, the slip vector and the dislocation line are parallel. On the other hand, the slip vector of an edge dislocation is perpendicular to the direction of the dislocation line.

Screw dislocations are classified as being "right-handed" or "left-handed." Perhaps the simplest and most general way of specifying whether a dislocation is of the right-handed or left-handed type is to use the following rule.[1] To test whether the dislocation is right-handed, place the extended right hand parallel to and on the right side of the slip plane with the fingers reaching in the direction of the shearing force operating on that side of the plane. If the outstretched thumb points in the direction of motion of the dislocation line, the dislocation is right-handed. If it points in the opposite direction, the dislocation is left-handed. Alternatively, one may make the same test with "left" substituted for "right" in the above rule. The dislocation in Fig. 15.8 evidently is right-handed.

BURGERS CIRCUIT AND BURGERS VECTOR

Conceivably, an edge dislocation might be more complicated than the example shown in Fig. 15.4 or several dislocations might be close together. A way of specifying the extent of dislocation in a region was devised by Burgers.[2] It is based on the idea of drawing rectangles in the region being investigated by connecting atoms as shown in Fig. 15.10. Such a rectangle is called a "Burgers circuit." If the region contains no dislocation, the rectangle made by connecting an equal number of atoms on opposite sides will close completely. On the other hand, if it contains one edge dislocation, it will fail to close by one interatomic distance as in Fig. 15.11. If the region should contain two dislocations, the

[1] I am indebted to Professor O. W. Albritton of Arlington State College for showing me this simple and helpful rule.

[2] Burgers is a Dutch scientist who has made extensive theoretical investigations of dislocations.

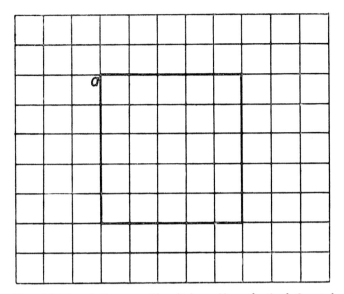

Fig. 15.10   A Burgers Circuit in a Hypothetical Crystal of Regular, or No Defect, Structure

The Burgers circuit starts at a. It is drawn 4 interatomic distances downward, 5 interatomic units of distance to the right, 4 units upward and 5 units to the left. The path laid out in this manner returns to its starting point. In dislocation language, the Burgers circuit is closed. This figure actually is intended to represent a plane of atoms with an atom located at each intersection.

Burgers circuit will fail to close by two interatomic distances. An arrow (vector) drawn from the terminal point of the Burgers circuit to its beginning measures the amount by which the circuit fails to close and, hence, is a measure of the total effect of any dislocations in the region. Such an arrow is called a "Burgers vector."

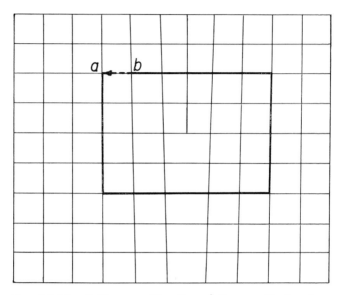

Fig. 15.11   A Burgers Circuit and Burgers Vector in a Hypothetical Crystal Containing an Edge Dislocation

The Burgers circuit is drawn in a plane perpendicular to the slip plane and to the dislocation line. If the distances are laid out as in the previous figure, the circuit goes only as far as b. An arrow drawn from b to a indicates the distance by which the circuit fails to close. The arrow is called a Burgers vector.

The idea of Burgers circuits and Burgers vectors is applicable to screw dislocations also. The heavy line in Fig. 15.8 may be imagined to be a Burgers circuit that starts at x and ends at y. The arrow extending from y to x is the Burgers vector that closes the circuit. One notes that it coincides with the slip vector described in the previous section.

DISLOCATIONS AND SLIP IN CRYSTALS

The passage of a dislocation through a crystal produces an offset with a width about equal to an atomic diameter. But microscopic observations have indicated that actual offsets may amount to 500 or even 1000 diameters or more. Such large relative movements of the two parts of a crystal might be imagined to be the result of the passage of a succession of dislocations along the same slip plane. Such an idea has some plausibility because crystals usually contain many dislocations. Furthermore, dislocations may enter a crystal from its surface which thus acts as a supplier of dislocations. An alternative is that the same dislocation passes repeatedly along the same slip plane.[3]

The explanation of repeated passage of the same dislocation is based on a mechanism of combined edge and screw dislocations. An example of such a type is presented in Fig. 15.12. On a magnified scale, the dislocation line AB in this figure would not appear as a simple curve but would be composed alternatively of short sections of edge dislocation and screw dislocation. To the concept of combined edge and screw dislocations is added the notion that such a dislocation may be "pinned" at a number of points because of the presence of foreign atoms or by some other irregularity in the structure of the metal. As an example, suppose that a dislocation line becomes pinned at two points. Between these points, the line continues to move because of some applied stress. The situation between the points is then as shown in Fig. 15.13A. Continued stress causes the line to bow out farther and swing around the pinning points as shown in Fig. 15.13B and Fig. 15.13C.[4]

---

[3] Those interested in studying this problem in more detail should refer to Read (6) and other books on dislocations.

[4] The action shown in these figures takes place in the crystal as was the situation in Fig. 15.13A but, for convenience, the crystal has been omitted.

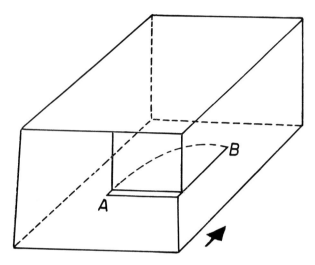

Fig. 15.12   A Curved Dislocation Line Involving Both Edge and Screw Dislocations

The figure represents a plane-sided crystal in which slip is beginning. The dislocation line *AB* is curved and has segments of both edge and screw dislocation. The small arrow at the lower right is a slip vector.

When the two parts of the dislocation line come together somewhere near *x* and *y*, they form a loop that continues to expand. The two stubs remain attached to the pinning points and develop a new bow as in Fig. 15.13E. Repetition of the process produces a series of roughly circular, more or less concentric dislocation loops. The combination of pinning points and moving dislocation lines has been described as a "Frank-Read source."

THE EXPERIMENTAL EVIDENCE FOR DISLOCATIONS

For some years, the concept of dislocations was little more than an unproven hypothesis. However, recent

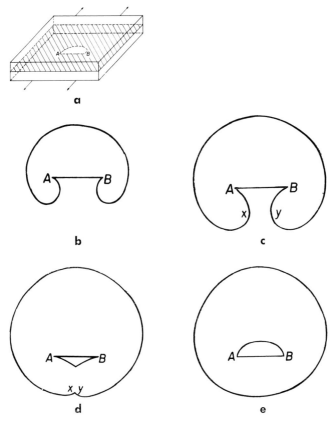

Fig. 15.13 Dislocation Loop Produced by a Frank-Read Source

a. This figure depicts a crystal in which a dislocation line is pinned fast at two points, *A* and *B*. A slight stress causes the line to bow out as shown.

b and c. These drawings show later stages in the billowing out of the dislocation line on the slip plane. (Crystal not shown.)

d. The lower bulges have made contact at points *x* and *y* and have joined together to form a complete loop. At the same time, the stubs from *A* and *B* have joined together.

e. A second bulge is starting from the swinging of the stubs from *A* and *B*. Eventually, it will produce another loop inside the one already generated.

The process described above can repeat itself to produce a great many loops.

experiments have given evidence of their actual existence.

An Example of Edge Dislocations

In some instances, the etching of metallographic specimens has produced rows of pits rather than a continuous
groove. An example of such pits in a piece of iron is
presented in Fig. 15.14. The pattern of pits suggests
strongly that the most prominent grain contains a

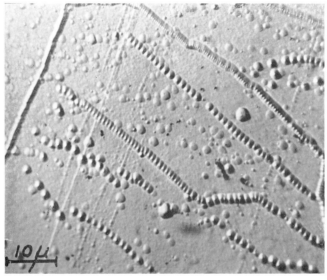

**Fig. 15.14   Etching Pits Outline Boundaries of Sub-
grains in a Piece of Iron**

Etching appears to be more rapid in the vicinity of an irregularity in the structure of a metal. Hence, etching pits are
taken to be an indication of dislocations. In this figure, the
pits appear to be the result of a situation like that illustrated
in the following two figures.
Boswell *(4)*.

number of subgrains like those described in Chapter 14. The orientation of subgrains characteristically deviates only slightly from what might be called the average orientation of the grain, and hence, from each other. One may imagine a relationship between two subgrains such as that pictured in Fig. 15.15. Both

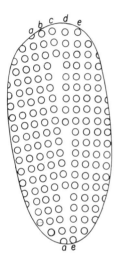

Fig. 15.15   The Junction Between Two Grains of Nearly the Same Orientation

Both grains have planes that are perpendicular to the plane of the paper but the planes in one grain lack a few degrees of being parallel to corresponding planes in the other. As a consequence, an entire series of planes terminates at the boundary between the grains as illustrated by planes *b*, *c*, and *d*. Situations similar to the one depicted here are likely to exist between two adjoining subgrains.

grains have planes of atoms that are perpendicular to a common plane, the plane of the paper. Further, these planes lack being parallel by only a fraction of a degree —the angle is magnified in the figure. The result will be that some planes will terminate at the junction of the grains as illustrated (planes *b, c,* and *d*). The terminal edges of these planes will constitute a series of edge dislocations as is evident from the conventionally drawn Fig. 15.16. The pits occur because etching reagents commonly act most energetically where an irregularity occurs in the polished surface.

The Motion of Dislocations

Evidence for the existence and motion of dislocations of the combined edge and screw type actually appeared in the electron micrograph shown in Fig. 2.9. The markings in this figure appear to be "footprints" of dislocation lines. Actual motion of such lines has been photographed when the specimen was stressed while in the

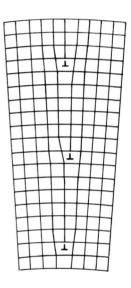

Fig. 15.16   The Junction Between Two Grains of Nearly the Same Orientation as Depicted in a Conventional Dislocation Drawing

If the situation depicted in the previous figure is illustrated by a drawing of the type commonly used in publications on dislocations, the result is the three positive dislocations seen in this figure.

electron microscope. A still picture showing series of dislocation lines in aluminum and the offsets they produce as they leave the crystal is presented in Fig. 15.17. The tensile forces on the thin crystal were as indicated in the figure. S_1, S_2, and S_3 are steps at the edge of the crystal. They were formed at the ends of slip planes by dislocations that passed out of the crystal. At S_2 and S_3 all of the dislocations appear to have been drained out but at the left of the micrograph some are still present and appear to be moving toward S_1. Dislocations

Fig. 15.17   Steps Formed in the Side of an Aluminum Crystal by the Passage of Dislocations

The steps were caused by the application of tensile forces that operated in a right-left direction. Apparently, dislocations moved along the slip planes from left to right and passed out of the crystal at S_1, S_2, and S_3. The micrograph suggests that the dislocations are completely drained from S_2 and S_3. They are still numerous along the slip plane associated with S_1 but the step at that point indicates that some of them have already passed out.

Berghezan and Fourdeux (5).

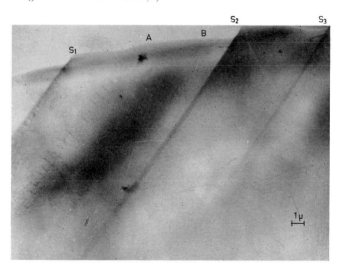

appear also to be moving toward points A and B. They may be the cause of the slight shift in direction at the edge of the crystal in the vicinity of A.

REFERENCES

1. R. O. Simmons and R. W. Balluffi: "Measurements of Equilibrium Vacancy Concentrations in Aluminum," *Physical Review,* Vol. 117, 1960, pp. 52–61.

2. J. E. Bauerle, C. E. Klabunde, and J. S. Koehler: "Increase in Resistivity in Water-Quenched Gold," *Physical Review,* Vol. 102, 1956, p. 1182.

3. J. E. Bauerle and J. S. Koehler: "Quenched-in Lattice Defects in Gold," *Physical Review,* Vol. 107, 1957, pp. 1493–1498.

4. F. W. C. Boswell: "Observations on the Dislocation Structure of Subboundaries in Iron," *Proceedings,* American Society for Testing Materials, Vol. 57, 1957, pp. 521–526.

5. Aurel Berghezan and Angeline Fourdeux: "Transmission Electron Microscopy Studies of the Mechanism of Plastic Deformation," *Journal of Applied Physics,* Vol. 30, 1959, pp. 1913–1922.

6. W. T. Read, Jr.: "Dislocations in Crystals," McGraw-Hill Book Company, Inc., New York, 1953.

CHAPTER 16

Metals in Nuclear Reactors

WHEN THE FISSIONING of uranium became of military and industrial importance, metallurgists discovered that they were confronted with a new set of problems. They had been aware of an extensive area of knowledge related to radioactivity that dated back to Becquerel and the Curies. They knew, for example, that uranium of atomic weight 238—usually designated as uranium-238 or as U^{238}—disintegrated through a series of products of which the better known were radium-226, radon-222, and polonium-210. The series ended with the nonradioactive element lead having an atomic weight 206[1]. These things, however, were considered to be within the province of the physicists. The metallurgical aspects appeared to be of minor importance.

Three radioactive, chemical elements, all metals, find use in nuclear reactors because of their capacity to be fissioned if conditions are appropriate. The first to be

_____
[1] Uranium-235 also disintegrates through a series of radioactive elements. This series, likewise, ends with the nonradioactive element lead but, in this instance, the atomic weight (mass number) is 207.

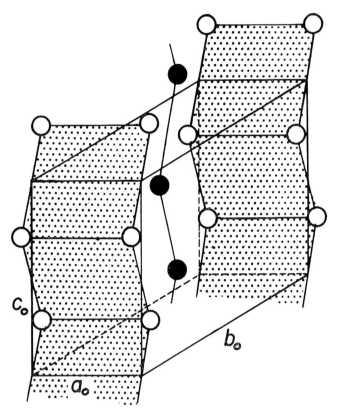

Fig. 16.1   The Unit Cell of Uranium

This cell is orthorhombic, that is, each edge is perpendicular to the other two but edges in different directions are unequal in length. Unlike unit cells shown previously, the corners are not occupied by atoms although the cell can be drawn in such a way that they are. The atoms lie in zig-zag paths along directions parallel to the c_o (z) axis. They may also be imagined to lie on corrugated planes that extend in the a_o and c_o directions and are stacked in the b_o direction. Portions of such planes are shown at the ends of the cell. The atoms represented by filled circles lie in the c_o direction through the center of the cell. They may be considered to lie on an imaginary, or phantom, plane like the planes at the ends of the cell.

used in a reactor was uranium. It is still the most important. Accordingly it will be considered first and in most detail.

URANIUM

Uranium is interesting from the engineering point of view mainly because it is fissionable. Metallurgically, it is unattractive. Its mechanical properties leave much to be desired; its resistance to corrosion is worse than unsatisfactory; if added to other metals, it rarely improves their properties; and it is expensive. On the other hand, its physical characteristics are both unusual and interesting. Even if the metal were not the backbone of the nuclear industry, it would be worthy of study for scientific reasons.

Crystalline Nature of Uranium

Often, the description of a metal begins with a statement concerning its crystal structure. Uranium has a unit cell of which the form is a rectangular parallelopiped as shown in Fig. 16.1. In Chapter 3, the cell was described as orthorhombic, that is, with its edges at right angles to each other but of different length in each direction. The figure shows that the atoms do not lie on lattice points. Actually, the cell can be so drawn that lattice points are occupied. Crystallographers have considerable leeway in assigning unit cells to a substance and often base their decisions on convenience. With the aid of the side view of the cell presented in Fig. 16.2, one sees that the atoms may be imagined to lie on corrugated sheets. The sheets are stacked in the b_o direction with atoms in any sheet meshing into the interstices of adjoining sheets.

Reference was made in Chapter 11 to the existence of two allotropic transformations in uranium. An equiva-

ig. 16.2 shows how the cell appears when viewed from the de. At 25°C., the dimensions of the unit cell are: $a_o = 2.854$ $b_o = 5.869$ Å, and $c_o = 4.956$ Å.

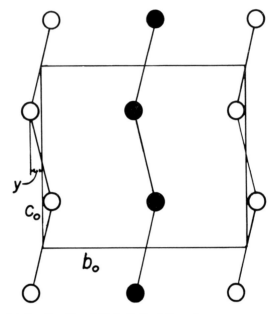

Fig. 16.2   Profile of Unit Cell of Uranium

The cell as seen by an observer looking the a_o (x) direction. He sees the traces of the zig-zag planes as indicated here. Atoms at the ends of the cell may be imagined to lie in the plane of the paper. The string of atoms through the center lies a distance $a_o/2$, or half the width of the unit cell, below the plane of the paper, or above it if one prefers. The zig-zag effect as indicated by distance y actually is greater than indicated by the drawing.

lent statement is that uranium may exist in any of three allotropic forms. The one that has just been described is, of course, the low temperature form customarily called α uranium. When heated, α uranium transforms at 665°C. into a different arrangement of atoms known as β uranium. This form persists over only a narrow range of temperature. At 770°C. it is converted into γ uranium. Beta uranium has a complex structure which requires for its representation a tetragonal unit cell containing 30 atoms. By contrast, the orthorhombic cell of α uranium has a volume corresponding to only 4 atoms and the body-centered cubic unit cell of γ uranium can accommodate only the equivalent of 2 atoms.

Physical Properties of Uranium

A peculiarity of uranium that seems to be related to the stacking of sheets of atoms is that when a crystal of uranium is heated, the distance between sheets decreases. The sheets themselves increase in area. The consequence of this behavior is evident in Fig. 16.3 which shows the change in length with temperature in the three directions parallel to the edges of the unit cell.

Another oddity of uranium is that its thermal conductivity increases with temperature instead of decreasing as in ordinary metals. This fact is taken as an indication that uranium is not completely metallic in nature.

As might be anticipated, changes in properties occur at both transformations. For example, the electrical resistance of a uranium wire decreases suddenly as the temperature rises through 665°C. and decreases again at the 770°C. transformation. To metallurgists, perhaps the most important change is related to hardness. As Fig. 16.4 shows, the hardness increases suddenly when α uranium is converted to the β condition but at 770°C. drops to a very low value. The changes would appear even more striking if the graph in Fig. 16.4 were plotted with regular instead of logarithmic coordinates. A consequence of the relatively high hardness of β uranium is that fabricating operations such as forging and rolling usually are performed with the metal in either the α or the γ condition. Whatever the temperature, some protection against oxidation is highly desirable. Small pieces of uranium can burn briskly in air.

Fig. 16.3   The Thermal Expansion of a Crystal of Uranium in the Three Directions, a_0, b_0, and c_0

This diagram shows that the crystal actually shortens in the direction specified as b_o in Fig. 16.1, that is, in the direction in which the sheets of atoms are piled. This difference of expansion in different directions undoubtedly is a factor in the tendency of a uranium rod to deform when heated and cooled through a number of temperature cycles. It, probably, is less important than the effect of the transformations, however. Modified from Bridge, Schwartz, and Vaughan (1).

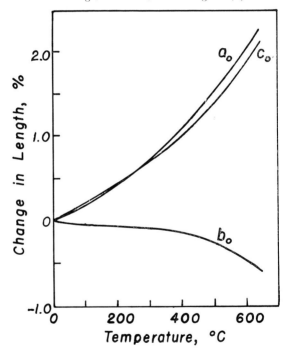

The Fissioning of Uranium

As mentioned previously, its capacity to fission is the reason for the importance of uranium. Not all atoms of uranium can be fissioned readily, however. In ordinary

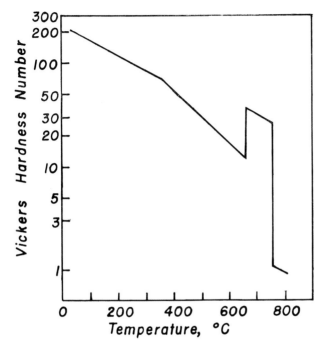

Fig. 16.4 The Change in Hardness of Uranium With Temperature

The logarithmic scale on which the hardness values are plotted tends to obscure the extreme differences in hardness. Gamma uranium is extremely soft. The β range usually is avoided in fabricating operations. Should an attempt be made to fabricate a piece of uranium while it is partly in the β form and partly in the α or γ form, differences in hardness and strength of the two portions may cause differences in the degree of deformation of the two portions and hence to tearing or other damage. The change of direction slightly below 400°C. probably means that recrystallization and associated softening become rapid at this temperature. Similar kinks have been observed in the hardness curves of other metals.

Chubb *(2)*.

uranium as produced from ore, only slightly more than 0.7% can. The reason for this situation is that ordinary uranium contains two kinds of atoms. Both of them are alike chemically, but they differ in weight. The more plentiful kind weigh 238 on the atomic scale whereas the less plentiful kind, the fissionable variety, weigh only 235. The two kinds are known as U^{238} and U^{235} respectively.

Both kinds of uranium atoms are composed of protons and neutrons as are the atoms of other elements. A nucleus of U^{238} contains 146 neutrons and 92 protons. A nucleus of U^{235} has the same number of protons but only 143 neutrons. Fissioning of a nucleus of U^{235} takes place when it is struck by a slowly moving neutron set free by a previously fissioned atom. The behavior of the two kinds of atoms is depicted in the three drawings[2] of Fig. 16.5. The second drawing shows an atom disintegrating into two main fragments plus a few free neutrons. It is these neutrons released by the fissioning that are responsible for fissioning other atoms of U^{235} and thus making possible the indefinite continuation of the process.

In a reactor that is operated on ordinary uranium, so many of the neutrons escape from the uranium-bearing core or are absorbed by surrounding substances that the number available for fissioning is little more than enough to keep the reactor going. To provide a more comfortable margin of operation and permit greater variation in design some builders have the uranium (the fuel elements) enriched in U^{235}. Actually, the ratio of U^{235} to U^{238} can be varied over a wide range by artificial methods. If the proportion of U^{235} is made relatively high, the fissioning process can be very lively. In fact, care

---

[2] The little character shown in these drawings has been named Tom McEnergy. He is the brainchild of Carl Ver Steeg. The author is indebted to *Metal Progress* for permission to use the figures in which Tom appears.

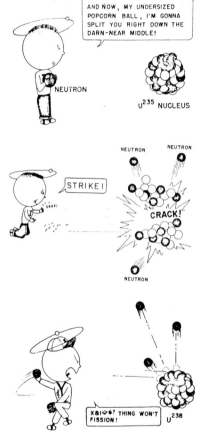

Fig. 16.5 Tom Mc-Energy Demonstrates the Difference in Fissionability of Uranium-235 and Uranium-238

Tom McEnergy eyes the nucleus of a uranium atom (U^{235}) which he intends to split. The nucleus is composed of two kinds of particles: protons (white) and neutrons (black).

In this figure, Tom has bowled his neutron into the nucleus. The obvious result is that the nucleus has split into two major fragments plus a few liberated, individual neutrons.

Tom has no success at all when he tries to cause fission of a nucleus of U^{238} by bowling neutrons against, or throwing them at, the nucleus.

must be taken, if the ratio is very high, not to have too much uranium in a small volume or an unwanted reaction, possibly an explosion, may take place.

An interesting question pertains to the fate of the two large fragments of a uranium atom that has undergone fissioning. The answer is that as the fragments are slowed down as the result of their efforts to push atoms of surrounding substances around, they pick up electrons and become atoms of elements of intermediate atomic weight. Effectively they produce a slight alloying in the uranium. As the two fragments formed from a single nucleus almost never are identical, they produce atoms of two different elements. The combined weight of the fragments set free from a nucleus must be equal to 235 minus the number of neutrons set free. This statement is valid only because a neutron has a mass of almost exactly one on the atomic scale. For example, if three neutrons are set free, the total weight of the two fragments must be 232.

Fragments do not settle down immediately to become peaceful atoms. What happens if, for example, a fragment has the correct weight to become an atom of tellurium is indicated by the sequence below:

Seq. 16.1

$$_{52}\text{Te}^{135} \xrightarrow[\text{2m}]{\beta^-} {}_{53}\text{I}^{135} \xrightarrow[\text{6.7h}]{\beta^-} {}_{54}\text{Xe}^{135}$$

$$\xrightarrow[\text{9.2h}]{\beta^-} {}_{55}\text{Cs}^{135} \xrightarrow[\text{20,000y}]{\beta^-} {}_{56}\text{Ba}^{135}$$

In sequences similar to the above, the particular nucleus involved frequently is identified not only by the chemical symbol but also by the total number of neutrons and protons combined (numerically equal to the weight of the nucleus) and by the number of protons alone (equal to the positive charge on the nucleus). Here, tellurium is indicated to have a combined total of 135 neutrons and protons of which 52 are protons. So U^{238} might be written as $_{92}U^{238}$. What Sequence 16.1 says is that the atom of tellurium gives off an electron (a negative β particle) and becomes an atom of iodine which, in turn, ejects an electron to become an atom of xenon and so on through cesium to barium which is stable, that is, not radioactive. The rate at which these elements are converted to the next in the series is indicated by the half-life times marked below the arrows. One observes that the conversion of tellurium to iodine is rapid. The half-life time of 2 minutes means that half of the tellurium atoms have already turned into iodine atoms after 2 minutes. On the other hand, half of the cesium still remains after 20,000 years. It is these atoms originating from the fission fragments that keep the fuel elements radioactive for so long a time after they have been removed from the reactor.

THORIUM

The inclusion of thorium with fissionable metals is not strictly correct. It is a radioactive element in the same sense that uranium is and disintegrates through a series of radioactive elements to become nonradioactive lead of atomic weight 208. It is not fissionable. It can be made so by exposure to neutrons in a reactor but when it has become fissionable, it is no longer thorium but has been converted to uranium. What happens to an atom of thorium when it is struck by and "absorbs" a neutron is indicated by the sequence

Seq. 16.2

$$_{90}\text{Th}^{232} + {_0}\text{n}^1 \longrightarrow {_{90}}\text{Th}^{233} \xrightarrow[23\text{m}]{\beta^-} {_{91}}\text{Pa}^{233} \xrightarrow[27.4\text{d}]{\beta^-} {_{92}}\text{U}^{233}$$

As shown by the half-life of 27.4 days in the protactinium to uranium step, the transition requires a considerable interval of time. Uranium-233 is fissionable in about the same way that U^{235} is. Also, it undergoes radioactive disintegration[3] much as other uranium isotopes.[4] The ter-

---

[3] Uranium-233 is not the first element of its radioactive series. It is an intermediate product in a chain of radioactive disintegration elements that begins with plutonium-241.

[4] Although the name "isotope" is used here for the first time, the idea is not new. An isotope of an element is one of the kinds of atoms of which it is composed. For example, U^{238} and U^{235} are isotopes of uranium. Pu^{239} and Pu^{241} are among the several isotopes of plutonium.

minal element of the series is nonradioactive bismuth of
weight 209. The metallurgical, physical, and chemical
properties of U^{233} are essentially identical with those of
U^{235} and U^{238}.

Properties of Thorium

If one were to select any property of thorium as being
of special interest, its high ductility might well be that
one. This characteristic is in accordance with its face-
centered cubic structure. In fabrication, thorium has the
ability to flow around any particles of oxide or other
material imbedded in it much like water flows around a
stone. Correspondingly, it has a low tensile strength and
is generally unsatisfactory as a structural material.
Furthermore, with the exception of a fractional percentage of carbon, the addition of alloying elements produces
little improvement in mechanical properties.

Thorium has a transformation at the relatively high
temperature of 1375°C. at which it becomes body-
centered cubic. Conversion into the high-temperature
form is accompanied by a pronounced rise in resistivity,
a behavior that is in marked contrast with the sudden
decrease in resistivity that is observed in some metals
under similar circumstances.

PLUTONIUM

In reactor metallurgy, plutonium usually means plu-
tonium-239. Other isotopes of plutonium exist—Pu^{241} is
not uncommon and may be associated with Pu^{239}—but
Pu^{239} is the fissionable isotope and is considered of major
importance. Plutonium is truly a manufactured metal
for what little can be found in nature is inconsequential.
To produce plutonium, one exposes U^{238} in a nuclear
reactor. The effect of the neutrons in the reactor on the

U^{238} is to convert it to Pu^{239} in accordance with the following sequence:

Seq. 16.3

$$_{92}U^{238} + {}_0n^1 \longrightarrow {}_{92}U^{239} \xrightarrow[23m]{\beta^-} {}_{93}Np^{239} \xrightarrow[2.3d]{\beta^-} {}_{94}Pu^{239}$$

What this sequence says is that when an atom of U^{238} absorbs a neutron, its weight is increased from 238 to 239. However, as the number of protons remains the same, the atom still behaves as an atom of uranium. Almost immediately, these atoms of U^{239} begin giving off electrons. The loss of an electron does not change the atomic weight but does increase the charge on the nucleus—or converts a neutron to a proton—so that the number of protons per nucleus is increased. Consequently, the chemical nature of the element is changed; the atom of uranium becomes an atom of neptunium. Ejection of a second electron from the nuclus converts the neptunium to plutonium. Obviously, if U^{238} is present in the reactor, plutonium is produced whether it is wanted or not. If the plutonium is wanted as a separate substance, it must be extracted from the uranium fuel elements by a chemical operation. One point which is not indicated by the sequence above is that the neutrons must have a proper speed if they are to be absorbed by the U^{238} atoms.

Plutonium is known as an alpha emitter, that is, its radioactivity consists only of the ejection of α particles. It is much more radioactive than either U^{235} or U^{233} and consequently is the most hazardous of the three fissionable substances with which to work. It is so radioactive that a block of the metal will melt from the heat

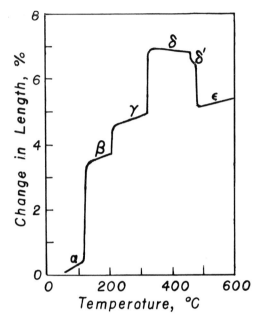

Fig. 16.6 The Expansion of Plutonium With Rising Temperature

Data for this graph were obtained from a specimen heated by its own radioactivity.

Cramer, Miner, Schonfeld, and Hawes *(3).*

generated by its own radioactivity unless that heat is drained away.

Plutonium is distinguished also for undergoing more allotropic transformations than any other metal. Fig. 16.6 depicts the sudden changes in length that occur as the metal is heated by its own radioactivity. Oddly enough, a block of plutonium actually shrinks as it is heated through the δ range, 320°C. to 440°C. On the graph, this behavior is made apparent by the negative (downward to the right) slope. What this negative slope means is that the coefficient of expansion is negative. Obviously, a similar situation exists in the δ′ range.

Fabrication of plutonium is complicated by the brittleness of both the α and β forms. Only when plutonium is heated into the γ phase is it sufficiently ductile for formation into shapes.

THE CAPACITY OF METALS FOR CAPTURING NEUTRONS

All materials, including those that are used in the construction of a nuclear reactor, absorb, or capture, neutrons in some degree. What proportion of the total number of neutrons produced by fissioning of U^{235} is absorbed by these materials is of extreme importance to the operation of a reactor. If the proportion is too high, so few neutrons will be available for splitting U^{235} atoms that the fissioning process can not be sustained. Regardless of how satisfactory its mechanical properties and its resistance to corrosion may be, a metal will be unusable if it captures too many neutrons. Capacity for capturing neutrons may be determined with reasonable accuracy. Its value turns out to be expressible in terms of area and usually is specified as a "capture cross section" of so many square centimeters, or in a new unit of area called the "fermi" which is equal to 10^{-24} square centimeters. A fermi is equal in area to the often used but inelegant name "barn."

If a reactor operates on natural uranium as all of the early reactors did, or, for that matter, on enriched uranium, U^{238} will be present and will absorb neutrons. Nothing can be done about the matter. Fortunately, the U^{238} does not capture a sufficient number of neutrons to prevent the operation of the reactor. As to all other substances that go into a reactor, some selection is possible.[5] For this reason, information such as that shown in Table 16.1 is valuable.

A glance at Table 16.1 makes evident the wide range of values of capture cross section among the metals. Also, it gives a clue as to why aluminum, magnesium, and zirconium are used so much in reactors especially as a jacketing material for the uranium fuel slugs. Beryllium is particularly satisfactory in several ways and undoubtedly would be used to a greater extent despite its high cost if it were not difficult to fabricate.

Both aluminum and magnesium lose strength at relatively low temperatures. Hence, fuel rods jacketed with them are limited as to maximum operating temperature. Even zirconium is limited both as to mechanical strength and resistance to corrosion at elevated temperatures. Its performance is improved by the addition of 2% or 3% of tin and fractional percentages of 2 or 3 other metals. A favored composition is known as Zircaloy-2.

Stainless steel has properties that are valuable in a power reactor but, as may be seen from Table 16.1, its component metals iron, chromium, and nickel all have relatively high capacities for absorbing neutrons. Consequently, its presence in the core of a reactor results in a serious loss of neutrons. Yet conditions sometimes arise that make its use advantageous in spite of the cost of enriching the uranium fuel to compensate for the loss of neutrons.

---

[5] Two important elements of a reactor usually do not involve metals. One of these is the moderator for slowing down the neutrons so that they will be effective in fissioning U^{235}. The other is the heat extracting medium which circulates among the uranium fuel elements to extract the heat developed by the fissioning process. The capture cross sections of both the moderator and the heat extractant are important and must be considered in the design of a reactor. Of course, if the uranium is enriched in U^{235} so that the neutrons are relatively abundant, the cross sections of the substances going into these items are not required to be so low. However, enrichment costs money.

TABLE 16.1—The Cross Sections of Some Materials of Interest
in Reactors

Material	Cross Section, Fermi*
Aluminum	0.23
Beryllium	0.01
Boron	651
Cadmium	2550
Chromium	2.9
Cobalt	37
Columbium	1.1
Copper	3.7
Europium	3980
Gadolinium	39800
Hafnium	105
Iron	2.5
Manganese	13
Magnesium	0.06
Nickel	4.6
Silver	62
Sodium	0.50
Tantalum	21
Tin	0.65
Zinc	1.0
Zirconium	0.18
Carbon	0.0045
Heavy water**	0.026
Ordinary water	0.66

* The values in this table are for "slow" or "thermal" neutrons
that have energies comparable with those of atoms of an ordinary
gas.

** Heavy water is water in which the hydrogen atoms of ordinary
water have been replaced by hydrogen atoms of twice the ordinary
weight. A gas composed of such atoms is called "deuterium." The
nucleus of an atom of deuterium is composed of a proton plus a
neutron instead of only a proton as in hydrogen.

THE NEED FOR CONTROL RODS

In the previous section, emphasis was put on the requirement of a low capacity for capturing neutrons. This
concentration on materials of low cross section does not

mean that those of high cross section are completely without interest under all circumstances. The value of a substance with high absorbing power becomes apparent as soon as one begins to consider what happens if more neutrons are generated than are needed. Suppose that at a particular instant a definite number of atoms undergo fissioning. The total number of neutrons released thereby is about 2.5 times the number of atoms that were fissioned. Hence, potentially, 2.5 times as many atoms could be fissioned in the next instant. However, for a particular reactor, capture by U^{238}, by jackets on the uranium fuel slugs, and by other parts plus the loss of neutrons by escape from the core may reduce the number available for fissioning to perhaps 1.03 times the number fissioned in the previous instant. Even with so small a factor, the rate of fissioning could build up rapidly. Then, heat would be developed at an excessive rate that would damage the reactor, or perhaps destroy it. Hence, for steady operation, some means must be found for reducing this multiplying factor from 1.03 to exactly 1. Several methods of control are available. The one most commonly used is the insertion of a neutron-absorbing substance near the fuel elements. Usually, the absorbing substance is attached to the end of a rod that may be thrust into the core for variable distances. Such a device is called a "control rod."

For the most satisfactory control, the density of neutrons should be reduced in such a way that the number of neutrons per cubic centimeter is about the same throughout the core. This condition cannot be fulfilled completely but may be approximated if the absorbing material is distributed advantageously as by use of a group of relatively small control rods.

Boron as a Control Rod Material

Also to be considered is the effect of the neutrons captured by a control rod material upon its capacity to continue capturing neutrons. The problem may be illustrated by an examination of boron, a commonly used absorber. Boron is composed of two isotopes, $_5B^{10}$ and $_5B^{11}$ (often written as B^{10} and B^{11}) which have capture cross sections of about 4000 fermi and 0.05 fermi, respectively. Because of its high absorbing power, B^{10} is responsible for the effectiveness of boron. B^{11} contributes almost no effect. This statement holds despite the fact that B^{11} atoms are more than 4 times as numerous as B^{10} atoms in a piece of boron. The effect of neutrons on B^{10} is indicated by the following sequence:

Seq. 16. 4
$$_5B^{10} + _0n^1 \longrightarrow _3Li^7 + _2He^4 + \text{radioactivity}$$

The sequence shows that when it captures a neutron, an atom of B^{10} vanishes and is replaced by two other atoms, one of lithium and one of helium. Neither of these elements has an absorbing power of any importance. Hence, every neutron captured reduces the capacity of the control rod for capturing neutrons by a small but definite amount. Eventually, the rod becomes ineffective and must be replaced.

Metallurgical Aspects of Boron

Boron is a metalloid rather than a metal. It is so brittle that it cannot be fabricated. Instead, it must be added as an alloying substance to some metal or incorporated into an assembly of some kind. One solution is to alloy it with stainless steel. It is not a perfect solution, however, as boron forms brittle compounds of relatively large volume in the steel. As the content of boron is increased, the larger amount of compound produces a marked deterioration in mechanical properties as indicated in Fig. 16.7. If as much as 2% of boron is added, the alloy becomes unworkable. In the event that the necessary neutron-absorbing capacity cannot be attained below about 2% boron, a trick must be used. The trick is to use boron in which the ratio of B^{10} to B^{11} has

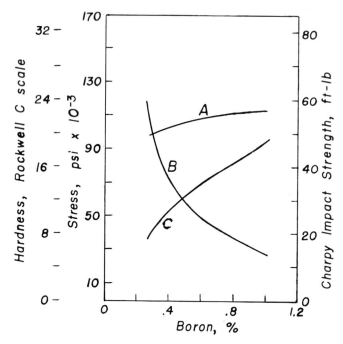

Fig. 16.7   The Deterioration of the Mechanical Properties of Stainless Steel as the Result of the Addition of Boron

A—Ultimate strength.
B—Charpy impact strength.
C—Rockwell C hardness.

Modified from a graph by Prus, Byron, and Thompson *(4)*.

been increased artificially. This scheme is practical but a bit expensive.

The steady loss of absorbing power of the B^{10} constituent as neutrons are captured imposes a limit on the life of a boron type control rod. However, the capturing of neutrons affects the control rods in another way.

Sequence 16.4 shows that capture of a neutron causes an atom of boron-10 to disappear and be replaced by two other atoms, one of lithium and one of helium. Both of these atoms are larger than the original boron atom. Furthermore, helium is an inert gas and its atoms tend to assemble together and form cavities. The result is an expansion of the boron-containing alloy which may swell to such a degree that the control rod is inclined to stick in its guide. When this condition is reached, replacement of the rod with a new one becomes imperative.

Hafnium As a Control Rod Material

Although the main features of a control rod material have been illustrated by the above description of boron rods, some mention should be made of the frequently used hafnium rods. Hafnium is expensive but it has interesting properties. It can be fabricated without serious difficulty and it is resistant to the types of corrosion that occur in reactors. Furthermore, its capacity for catching neutrons is such that no alloying with a metal of low capture cross section is needed. It is not embrittled noticeably by neutrons or other types of radiation occurring in a reactor, as are some metals, and control rods made of it have a relatively long life.

The reason for the relatively long life of hafnium as a control rod material is related to the capture cross sections of its 5 isotopes as indicated in Table 16.2.

TABLE 16.2—The Isotopes of Hafnium and Their Capture Cross Sections

Number	Weight on Atomic Scale	Percentage of Total Atoms	Capture Cross Section, Fermi
1	176	5.2	15
2	177	18.5	380
3	178	27.2	75
4	179	13.8	65
5	180	35.3	13

From a glance at this table, one sees that the isotope of weight 177 has the greatest capacity for capturing neutrons. Its cross section, 380, is about five times as great as that of the isotope with next largest cross section, Hf^{178}. The ratio of the number of neutrons captured, or absorbed, by these two isotopes is less than 5, however, because of the greater abundance of Hf^{178}. Suppose that an atom (nucleus) of Hf^{177} does capture a neutron. It will become an atom of Hf^{178} as indicated by the following sequence:

Seq. 16.5

$$_{72}Hf^{177} + {_0}n^1 \longrightarrow {_{72}}Hf^{178} + \text{gamma ray}$$

The new atom of Hf^{178} emits a gamma ray as it is formed but it is not radioactive. The piece of hafnium in which this event occurred has a lower total absorbing capacity because the cross section of the new atom is only 75 fermi. Should an atom of Hf^{176} capture a neutron and be converted to Hf^{177}—a less probable event—the total absorbing power of the hafnium would be increased accordingly. The conclusion to be drawn is that the effectiveness of a hafnium control rod decreases with time of service less rapidly than a boron control rod does.

HOW RADIATION AFFECTS REACTOR MATERIALS

The consequences of the absorption of a neutron have been illustrated for boron and hafnium in the previous section. The neutrons concerned had been moving at a relatively slow speed at the time of capture. Hence, pure mechanical impact was not an important factor. Mechanical action is a major factor, however, when high speed fragments and neutrons that have just been released by fissioning encounter metals or other substances in a reactor.

Changes in Fuel Elements

Probably the most spectacular results of fissioning take place in the fuel elements, particularly in the uranium itself. The mechanical properties are altered noticeably.

Hardness increases and ductility decreases. A moderate rise in ultimate tensile strength takes place and the yield strength is increased by a factor of two or more. A major cause of these changes probably is the forcing of the atoms out of their normal positions by the passage of the fragments. This effect cannot be detected readily in the uranium but paths made by fragments can be observed in mica. Figure 16.8 shows a number of trails made by fission fragments in a piece of mica that had been placed adjacent to uranium which was undergoing fissioning. The picture was made with an electron microscope. Its magnification is 40,000 diameters.

Another effect of the fissioning process in uranium is an increase in volume. Part of this may be the result of the creation of two lighter atoms from one uranium

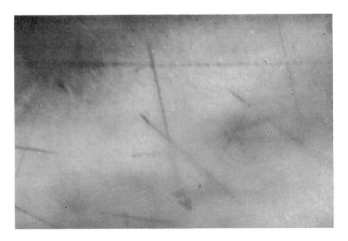

Fig. 16.8   Paths of Uranium Fission Fragments in a Sheet of Mica

The uranium was placed closely against the mica sheet and bombarded with neutrons to produce fissioning of the U^{235} present.

Silk and Barnes (5).   Magnification, 40,000 $\times$

atom. Part, also, may arise from the passage of the fragments as described in the previous paragraph. However,
the formation of the inert and insoluble gases krypton
and xenon from fission fragments appears to be the
major cause. Atoms of these gases gather in cavities and
produce a porous character in the metal as shown in Fig.
16.9. Problems related to the swelling and distortion of

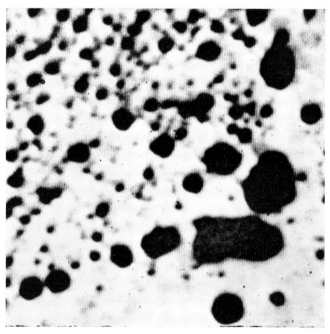

**Fig. 16.9   Cavities in Uranium Which Has Been in
Service in a Reactor**

These cavities probably were developed by the formation of
xenon and krypton gases from fission fragments. This photomicrograph was taken by television because the uranium was
too radioactive to be handled in the ordinary way.
Ball (6).   Magnification, 600×

fuel rods containing uranium have caused reactor engineers to investigate compounds of uranium such as the more rigid and already porous oxide.

Action of Fast Neutrons on Steel

Many reactor cores are surrounded by steel pressure vessels. How these vessels and other steel parts of a reactor are affected by the fast neutrons that strike them is a matter of some importance. The bombardment has been found to reduce the ductility and increase the yield strength considerably but the most striking result is the

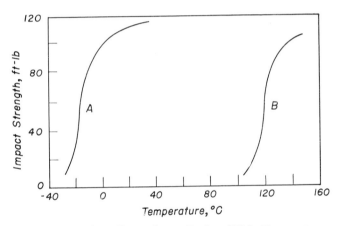

Fig. 16.10   The Effect of Irradiation With Neutrons on the Temperature of the Brittle-Ductile Transition

   Curve *A*—Specimen before irradiation.
   Curve *B*—Specimen after irradiation with high speed neutrons.

Temperature of the specimens during bombardment was below 95°C. Specimens were standard Charpy (V notch) impact type. They were cut from forged steel of the composition: 0.19% carbon, 0.40% chromium, 0.79% nickel, 0.64% molybdenum.

Graph is a modification of one by Hawthorne *(7)*.

increase in the temperature of the brittle-ductile transition in plain carbon and low alloy steels. Such steels frequently are brittle at low temperature but become ductile if heated.

The condition of brittleness or ductility usually is judged by the amount of energy necessary to break a specimen into two pieces in an impact test. If only a little energy is required to break it, the steel is considered to be brittle. If greater energy is required, the metal may be considered to have a degree of ductility. The appearance of the fractured surface usually is of some significance also. The temperature about halfway between the brittle and ductile conditions is called the transition temperature. Curves representing the change from the brittle to the ductile state in a low-alloy steel are shown in Fig. 16.10. Curve A is for the steel before irradiation and curve B for the same steel after irradiation with high energy neutrons.

A point of importance is that the effects of bombardment can be almost or completely eliminated if the irradiated piece is heated to a temperature of perhaps $500°$ C. Also, if the material is at a relatively high temperature at the time it is irradiated, the embrittling action is less than for a lower temperature.

REFERENCES

1. J. R. Bridge, C. M. Schwartz, and D. A. Vaughan: "X-Ray Diffraction Determination of the Coefficients of Expansion of Alpha Uranium," *Transactions,* American Institute of Mining, Metallurgical and Petroleum Engineers, Vol. 206, 1956, pp. 1282–1285.

2. W. Chubb: "Contribution of Crystal Structure to the Hardness of Metals," *Transactions,* American Institute of Mining and Metallurgical Engineers, Vol. 203, 1955, pp. 189–192.

3. E. M. Cramer, W. N. Miner, F. W. Schonfeld, and L. L. Hawes: see page 250 of Tipton *(8)*.

4. L. B. Prus, E. S. Byron, and J. F. Thompson: "Boron Stainless Steel Alloys," *Nuclear Science and Engineering,* Vol. 4, 1958, pp. 415–428.

5. E. C. H. Silk and R. S. Barnes: "Examination of Fission Fragment Tracks With an Electron Microscope," *Philosophical Magazine,* Series 8, Vol. 4, 1959, pp. 970–972.

6. J. G. Ball: "Metallurgical Research in Nuclear Power Production," *Journal,* Institute of Metals, Vol. 84, 1955–56, pp. 239–250.

7. J. R. Hawthorne: "Studies of Radiation Effects and Recovery of Notch Ductility of Pressure-Vessel Steels," a chapter in "Steels for Reactor Pressure Circuits," Special Report No. 69 of The Iron and Steel Institute, London, 1961, pp. 343–369.

8. C. R. Tipton, Jr. (Editor): "Reactor Handbook Volume 1—Materials," Interscience Publishers, New York, 2nd Ed., 1960.

9. Samuel Glasstone: "Sourcebook on Atomic Energy," D. van Nostrand Company, Inc., New York, 2nd Ed., 1958.

10. Irving Kaplan: "Nuclear Physics," Addison-Wesley Publishing Company, Inc., Reading, Massachusetts, 1958.

Terms in Alloy Diagrams

AN EXPLANATION of some terms used in connection with alloy diagrams is presented here for the information of those not already familiar with them.

The first term is "phase." This word is a physical chemist's term for a substance or material. However, it has a more specific meaning than either substance or material. First, a phase must be uniform in composition, a condition not necessarily true of a substance. Second, it must be at the same temperature at all points. Actually, as a matter of convenience in description, the word phase is sometimes stretched to include substances that do not satisfy the above requirements completely.

The requirement indicated above that a phase be everywhere uniform in composition has the corollary that if two or more phases exist side by side, one cannot merge gradually into the other; the boundary between them must be sharp. For example, in a vessel containing water and ice, the phase called water cannot merge gradually into the phase called ice. Of course, common experience tells one that the pieces of ice have a definite boundary against the water. Even though the ice in the vessel is present as a number of pieces, it is called, collectively, the "ice phase." Similarly, a piece of metal like copper is made up of individual grains but is considered as a single phase and would be even if the grains were separated from each other.

A phase may be composed of any number of elements or substances. The requirement is that the mass of substance be uniform in composition and temperature. Simple examples are water and alcohol mixed together or water with salt dissolved in it. Either solution has the characteristics of a simple (single) substance; it is uniform in composition. A solid solution of nickel in iron is a phase. A compound constitutes a phase. It is uniform in composition whatever the amount present and behaves like a simple substance. Either a solid solution of two metals, or a compound between two metals appears as a simple substance, a phase, if examined under a microscope. If particles of compound are dispersed throughout a solid solution, a matrix, in the manner of the Θ particles in the aluminum-copper alloy in Fig. 8.8, the alloy is described as "two phase."

The terms single phase and two phase are used in connection with the different areas in alloy diagrams. In the copper-zinc diagram, Fig. 5.11, the area marked α and the area marked β are called "single-phase fields." The area between them is called a "two-phase field"—it is the $\alpha + \beta$ field—because an alloy having a composition lying in this field would appear under a microscope to be composed of two substances.

Two other terms are related to the naming of solid solutions in an alloy system. In the copper-zinc diagram, Fig. 8.11, α is called a "terminal solid solution" because its area lies at one side of the diagram. Similarly, β is called an "intermediate solid solution" because its area lies near the central portion of the diagram.

Glossary

Actinide rare earths   The series of chemical elements that follows actinium in the periodic table. They are all radio-active and some of them must be produced artificially.

Age hardening   A commonly used but less scientific name for *Precipitation hardening.*

Alloy diagram   A less specific name for *Constitutional diagram.*

Alpha iron   Ordinary (unalloyed) iron below 900°C. It has a body-centered cubic space lattice.

Ångstrom unit   A unit of length equal to 1/100,000,000 cm. It is abbreviated as Å.

Atomic per cent   With reference to a component of an alloy, the per cent of the total number of atoms that is contributed by the component.

Austenite   Iron-carbon alloy (steel) at a temperature at which it has a face-centered cubic lattice. Also other alloys of iron in the face-centered cubic condition.

[303]

Bainite A product obtained when austenite decomposes, or is transformed, at a temperature below that at which pearlite is formed but above that at which martensite is obtained.

Barn An alternative name for fermi.

Beta brass A copper-zinc alloy having a zinc content between 46 and 50%. At elevated temperatures, beta brass has a wider range of composition. The name is derived from the corresponding phase field in the constitutional diagram.

Body-centered cubic Refers to a type of cubic unit cell that has a lattice point at each corner and one in the center. In metallic elements that are described as being body-centered cubic, each lattice point is occupied by an atom.

Brittle-ductile range A range of temperature over which some metals, particularly ordinary steels, change from a brittle to a ductile condition.

Burgers circuit An approximate rectangle imagined to be drawn within a metal by going from one atom to the next one. Opposite sides have the same number of atomic intervals. If the circuit so drawn closes, no dislocation exists within the enclosed region. If it does not close, the region contains one or more dislocations. The number of atomic distances by which the circuit fails to close is a measure of the degree of irregularity in the region. It corresponds to the length of the Burgers vector.

Burgers vector The distance by which a Burgers circuit fails to close. It is measured from the final to the initial point of the circuit.

Capture cross-section An expression used to describe the capacity, expressible in units of area, of a substance for capturing free neutrons. Usually, it refers to slowly moving, or thermal, neutrons unless otherwise specified.

Cementite A metallographer's, or microscopist's, name for iron carbide. It is used especially in descriptions of the microscopic appearance of polished and etched steel specimens.

Close-packed hexagonal Also called hexagonal close-packed. Refers to a prismatic unit cell having a base in the form of a rhombus with 60 and 120° angles and a height that approaches, ideally, 1.63 times the length of an edge of the base. It has a lattice point at each corner. In metallic elements based on this lattice, an atom lies at each corner and another atom, not on a lattice point, is located at half height directly above the center of one of the two equilateral triangles into which the base may be divided.

Cold working The shaping of a metal by forging, rolling, or some other operation while it is at room, or only slightly elevated, temperature; more generally, working below the temperature of recrystallization.

Composition vertical A vertical line drawn in a constitutional diagram to indicate an alloy of definite composition.

Constitutional diagram A diagram that shows the temperatures at which alloys made of any proportion of two (or three) metals exist in the liquid or solid state, the temperatures at which transformations occur, the manner in which solid solubility changes with temperature, and other features of a system of alloys. In brief, a diagram that shows the temperature and composition ranges of the phases existing in an alloy system.

Control rod A rod made of material with a high capacity for catching neutrons that is used to control the rate of fissioning in a nuclear reactor.

Coring Nonuniformity of composition on a microscopic scale in an alloy formed by the solid solution of one metal (or more) in another. Portions that solidify first differ in composition from those that solidify later.

Creep The slow deformation of a metal under a stress smaller than that which will cause rupture in a relatively short time.

Crystal In metallurgy, a volume of metal throughout which the alignment of atoms remains the same. *Crystal* is used interchangeably with *Grain*.

Deep hardening A term used in connection with the hardening of steel. It indicates that the steel hardens (is converted to martensite) to a considerable depth below the surface. Rates of cooling necessary to harden such a steel are relatively low.

Deformation Straining of a metal to such a degree that the change of dimension is permanent. Deformation usually takes place by slipping action, sometimes by the formation of mechanical twins.

Dendrite A tree-shaped crystal of metal frequently seen in alloys. It results from the tendency of metallic crystals to grow in preferred directions.

Diffusion In metallurgical literature, diffusion usually refers to the movement of atoms among other atoms in a metal or alloy. It may also refer to the movement of atoms in the gaseous state, as in a vaporized metal.

Dislocation As applied to metals, a dislocation is an imperfection in a crystal caused by the failure of planes in two portions to match. Dislocations are closely related to slipping action.

Dislocation line A line that marks the position of a dislocation. It also indicates the boundary between the slipped and unslipped portions of a crystal.

Equilibrium diagram An alternative name for constitutional diagram.

Eutectic An alloy having the lowest melting temperature of any alloy in its range of composition, and characterized by the conversion of the liquid alloy into two solid constituents during the solidifying process.

Eutectoid reaction A process similar to that which takes place in the solidification of alloys that form a eutectic but occurring in the solid alloy. As an adjective, eutectoid may be applied to composition, microscopic appearance, and also to the typical arrangement of lines in the constitutional diagram.

Face-centered cubic A type of cubic unit cell which has a lattice point at each corner and at the center of each face. In metallic elements described as being face-centered cubic, each lattice point is occupied by an atom.

Fermi A unit of capture cross-section, that is, of the capacity of a substance for capturing free neutrons. It is equal to 10^{-24} square centimeters.

Ferrite Iron-carbon alloy (steel) under such conditions that it has a body-centered cubic lattice. Also, other alloys of iron having body-centered cubic lattices.

Fission The disintegration of an atom, as uranium, into two major fragments plus a few free electrons.

Frank-Read source A region of a crystal which if put under stress, appears to have the capacity to generate large numbers of dislocations.

Gamma iron Ordinary (unalloyed) iron in a temperature range from about 900 to 1400°C. It has a face-centered cubic space lattice.

Gamma loop In the diagram of the iron-chromium system and in diagrams of some other iron alloys, a loop formed by lines curving upward from the A_3 transformation point to meet those coming down from the A_4 point. The loop so formed encloses the region in which the alloys exist in the gamma, or face-centered cubic, condition.

Grain A volume of metal throughout which the alignment of atoms is the same. *Grain* is used interchangeably with *Crystal*.

Grain boundary The surface over which a grain is in contact with other grains in a metal. On an etched metal, the grain boundaries appear in section as a network of lines covering the surface.

Hardenability The depth to which steel will harden (be converted to martensite) when quenched under a specific set of conditions.

Intermetallic compound Compound of two metals having a characteristic crystal structure. It may or may not follow ordinary rules of valency.

Isothermal transformation   Transformation of steel from its high-temperature form to a low-temperature form at a constant temperature.

Isotope   One of a group of atoms making up a chemical element all of which have identical chemical properties but each having a different weight. For example, nickel is composed of atoms of five different weights: 58, 60, 61, 62, and 64. They are the isotopes of nickel. Radioactive isotopes of nickel having still different weights are known. They may be produced in a nuclear reactor.

Lanthanide rare earths   The series of chemical elements that follows lanthanum in the periodic table. All elements in the group show a remarkable similarity in chemical behavior.

Lattice   An abbreviation for *Space lattice*.

Lattice parameter   The distance between successive points in a space lattice measured in a direction parallel to one of the three principal axes. A space lattice has three parameters of which all may be different, all may be equal, or two may be equal.

Lattice point   A point in a space lattice. For any substance, the arrangement of atoms about any lattice point is the same as about any other lattice point.

Law of levers   A formula for computing the amount of each of two constituents present in an alloy. To use the formula one must know the composition of each constituent and the composition of the alloy as a whole. The law is used mostly in connection with constitutional diagrams.

Liquidus line   A line in a binary constitutional diagram that gives the temperature at which an alloy of any composition begins to solidify.

Martensite   The product obtained when steel is quenched with sufficient rapidity to make it transform at a low temperature.

Miller indices A set of numbers that indicate the orientation of a plane of atoms with respect to a set of reference coordinates.

Miscibility gap In a liquid alloy, an interval of composition over which the two liquid metals will not combine into a single liquid but form two layers. The name is related to the corresponding lines in the alloy diagram. The gap may be limited to a narrow range of composition or may extend practically the full width of the diagram. The same term is applicable to solid alloys as when a solid solution breaks into two constituents over an interval of composition.

Monotectic reaction During solidification of an alloy, a reaction in which a liquid is converted to a solid plus a liquid of composition different from the original liquid. The reaction takes place in a reverse sense upon heating.

Monotectoid reaction An event in a solid alloy that resembles the monotectic reaction in a solidifying alloy.

Neumann band A type of mechanical twin produced in iron when it is struck a sudden, hard blow.

Nuclear reactor An assemblage of uranium and other materials which permits the fissioning of uranium to proceed indefinitely at a controlled rate and ordinarily provides a means of draining off the heat developed by the fissioning.

Ordering A change in an alloy during which the atoms of each component take up definite positions with respect to the atoms of the other component. The ordered state of an alloy is the opposite of the state in which the two kinds of atoms are distributed at random.

Pearlite The product that results when slowly cooling steel transforms at about 720°C. It is composed of alternate laminae of iron and iron carbide.

Per cent reduction A term used to specify the decrease in thickness of a sheet of metal being put through a rolling mill, or the decrease in cross-sectional area of a wire passed through a drawing die.

Peritectic reaction   A process, or reaction, that takes place during the solidification of an alloy in which two substances (phases) react to produce still a third substance. The reaction can take place in the reverse sense upon heating.

Peritectoid reaction   An event in a solid alloy that resembles the peritectic reaction of a solidifying alloy.

Phase   A mass of material that is physically and chemically homogeneous. Solid phases in an alloy may be elemental metals, solid solutions, or compounds.

Phase diagram   An alternative name for constitutional diagram.

Polycrystalline   An adjective used to describe a metal composed of several or many crystals as contrasted with one that is a single crystal.

Polygonization   The breaking up of a grain into subgrains.

Precipitation hardening   Also called *Age hardening*. The hardening of an alloy that results from the formation of tiny particles of a new constituent (phase) within a solid solution.

Radiation   In nuclear terminology, an inclusive term used to indicate the particles and electromagnetic radiation that are given off from radioactive substances and from devices such as nuclear reactors.

Radioactivity   A property possessed by some chemical elements and by nuclear devices that causes them to emit particles such as alpha and beta particles and electromagnetic (gamma) rays.

Recovery   A decrease over a period of time of the stresses induced in steel or other metal during a cold working operation. Usually, low-temperature heating is used to bring about recovery.

Recrystallization   Formation of new crystals in a cold worked metal or alloy.

Season cracking   A type of cracking that occurs in cold worked brass.

Shallow hardening   A term used in connection with the quenching of steel. It indicates that a piece of such steel can be hardened, that is made martensitic, only at and a little below the surface even by drastic quenching.

Sigma phase   A compound that forms in iron-chromium alloys having a composition near to the proportions of 50 atomic per cent of each element. It forms slowly and at relatively low temperatures by the decomposition of the previously existing alpha solid solution.

Single-phase field   An area on an alloy diagram that represents compositions that exist as a single substance, or a single phase, and appear as a single substance under the microscope.

Slip   The movement of one part of a crystal with respect to another along a plane called the *slip plane.*

Slip vector   In dislocation theory, a vector that indicates the direction of slip. It is parallel to the corresponding Burgers vector.

Solid solution   A type of alloy, or a constituent of an alloy, in which the atoms of one metal are distributed in a random fashion among the atoms of the other. Under a microscope, a solid solution is not distinguishable from an elemental metal.

Solidus line   A line in a binary constitutional diagram that gives the temperature at which an alloy of any composition begins to melt.

Solvus line   A line in a constitutional diagram that indicates the limit of solubility of one phase in another at any temperature.

Space lattice   A set of geometric points imagined to be superimposed on a crystalline substance in such a way that the group of atoms surrounding any point in the set is the same as the group surrounding any other point of the set. The lattice points lie on lines parallel to a set of three-dimensional, reference axes.

Spheroidite A particular type of structure that appears under the microscope as rounded particles of iron carbide embedded in ferrite (alpha iron). It is obtained when steel is tempered at a relatively high temperature.

Subgrains Portions of a parent grain that have nearly but not exactly the same orientation as other subgrains within the same grain.

Tempering The process that takes place when hardened (martensitic) steel is heated to a few hundred degrees. The steel loses some hardness and strength but becomes much less brittle.

Transformation The change of a metal or alloy from one atomic arrangement to another. Sometimes, the word is used in a more general sense to refer to other changes in an alloy or metal.

Transmission electron micrograph A micrograph obtained with an electron microscope. It is obtained when the electron stream is made to pass through an extremely thin section of metal.

Twin Part of a grain that is oriented differently from, but has a definite crystallographic relationship to, the main body of the grain. A twin may be formed during annealing of a metal that has been deformed while cold. Such twins are called annealing twins and are abundant in many face-centered cubic metals. A twin may also develop as the result of mechanical stresses. Twins originating in this way are called mechanical twins. They are most likely to be found in close-packed hexagonal and body-centered cubic metals.

Two-phase field An area in an alloy diagram that corresponds to compositions that show two microscopic constituents.

Unit cell A geometric figure used to indicate the type of a space lattice being described. The movement of a unit cell can generate the space lattice. Usually, the unit cell is pictured with associated atoms.

Vacancy   A vacant space that exists in a metal when an atom is missing from the site it would ordinarily occupy. If several atoms are missing from adjacent sites, a multiple vacancy exists.

Veining   Markings on a polished and etched piece of metal that have some resemblance to grain boundaries but lie within the grains. They suggest the existence of subgrains.

Weight per cent   With reference to the amount of a component in an alloy, the per cent of the total weight that is contributed by the component.

Work hardening   Hardening that takes place when a metal is worked, or deformed, below the recrystallization temperature; in other words, the hardening that results from cold working.

Index